W9-AYH-177

BRIDGES®
IN MATHEMATICS

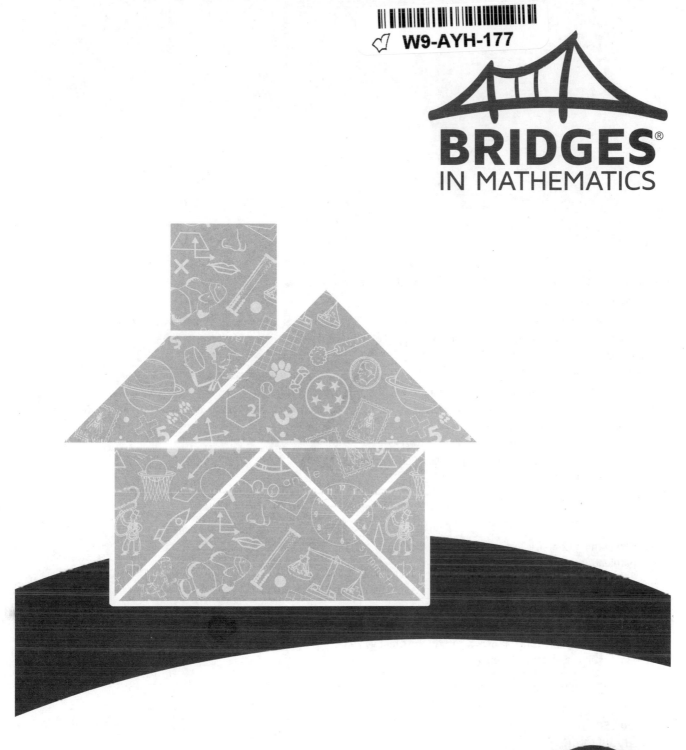

SECOND EDITION
HOME CONNECTIONS

GRADE 3

Published by  The MATH LEARNING CENTER Salem, Oregon

Bridges in Mathematics Second Edition Grade 3 Home Connections

The Bridges in Mathematics Grade 3 package consists of:

Bridges in Mathematics Grade 3 Teachers Guide Units 1–8

Bridges in Mathematics Grade 3 Assessment Guide

Bridges in Mathematics Grade 3 Teacher Masters

Bridges in Mathematics Grade 3 Student Book

Bridges in Mathematics Grade 3 Home Connections

Bridges in Mathematics Grade 3 Teacher Masters Answer Key

Bridges in Mathematics Grade 3 Student Book Answer Key

Bridges in Mathematics Grade 3 Home Connections Answer Key

Bridges in Mathematics Grade 3 Components & Manipulatives

Bridges Educator Site

Work Place Games & Activities

Number Corner Grade 3 Teachers Guide Volumes 1–3

Number Corner Grade 3 Teacher Masters

Number Corner Grade 3 Student Book

Number Corner Grade 3 Teacher Masters Answer Key

Number Corner Grade 3 Student Book Answer Key

Number Corner Grade 3 Components & Manipulatives

Word Resource Cards

Digital resources noted in italics.

The Math Learning Center, PO Box 12929, Salem, Oregon 97309. Tel 1 (800) 575-8130
www.mathlearningcenter.org

Prepared for publication using Mac OS X and Adobe Creative Suite.
Printed in the United States of America.

To reorder Home Connections, refer to number 2B3HC5 (package of 5).

QBB3903
06012020_LSC
Updated 2019-01-01.

Bridges in Mathematics is a standards-based K–5 curriculum that provides a unique blend of concept development and skills practice in the context of problem solving. It incorporates Number Corner, a collection of daily skill-building activities for students.

The Math Learning Center is a nonprofit organization serving the education community. Our mission is to inspire and enable individuals to discover and develop their mathematical confidence and ability. We offer innovative and standards-based professional development, curriculum, materials, and resources to support learning and teaching. To find out more, visit us at www.mathlearningcenter.org.

ISBN 978-1-60262-424-5

Bridges Grade 3
Home Connections

© The Math Learning Center | mathlearningcenter.org

Unit 5
Multiplication, Division & Area

Unit 6
Geometry

Unit 7
Extending Multiplication & Fractions

Unit 8
Bridge Design & Construction: Data Collection & Analysis

🏠 Addition Fact Review page 1 of 2

Note to Families

As a classroom teacher, I appreciate the ways in which families contribute to their children's success in school. When you take the time to review your child's schoolwork, talk about your child's day, and practice concepts and skills, you play an important role in your child's education.

In math class, we have been reviewing patterns in basic addition facts. We have reviewed helpful strategies and identified facts we already know. This assignment is intended to be a review and will give students an opportunity to share strategies with you that will later be used with larger numbers.

1 Complete these Doubles and Make Ten facts.

4	6	9	8	7	5	9
+ 4	+ 4	+ 9	+ 2	+ 7	+ 5	+ 1
8	1 0	1 8	1 0	1 4	1 0	1 0

2 Complete these Doubles Plus or Minus One facts.

5	7	3	4	8	9	6
+ 4	+ 8	+ 2	+ 3	+ 9	+ 10	+ 5
9	15	5	7	17	90	11

3 6 + 1 and 7 + 2 are examples of Count On facts. Write three more Count On facts.

8 + 3   9 + 4   10 + 5

4 Kallie thinks that every Doubles problem will have an even sum. Do you agree or disagree? Explain why.   I agree because ever doubles wc have a even mumber no matter what

5 The sum of two numbers is 12. List three possible equations.

a __9__ + __3__ = 12   **b** __10__ + __2__ = 12   **c** __11__ + __1__ = 12

6 Write an equation that could represent this picture.

(continued on next page)

Addition Fact Review page 2 of 2

7 Emma says that she can prove that 8 + 3 = 7 + 4. How could she use a number rack to prove her thinking? Draw a number rack or explain in writing.

yes   because if you 8+3 it equal 11

and   7+4 also 11 so they are

equal

8 **CHALLENGE** Solve the problem in the easiest way you can. Show your work. (Hint: Change the order in which you add the numbers.)

60 + 50 + 40 + 70 + 30 =

70 + 60 + 50 + 40 + 30

130 + 90 + 30

320 + 30

360

9 **CHALLENGE** Sage wants to buy board games for some of her friends. Board games cost $9 each. She has $6 and one coupon for $3 off. Her Aunt Barbara gave her $7 and another coupon for $3 off.

a How many games can Sage buy if she uses the coupons? Show your work.

9 + 7 + 3   19

②

b Will Sage have any money left over? If so, how much? Show your work.

①

Yer she has 1 $

left

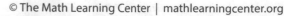

NAME _____ | **DATE** _____

🏠 Addition & Subtraction Review page 1 of 3

Note to Families

Students have reviewed and explored addition facts and strategies, and they are now investigating subtraction facts. Naming, categorizing, and identifying strategies will help your child not only understand and solve basic subtraction facts but also solve larger subtraction problems. These strategies help students develop a better understanding of the relationship between numbers and operations. Encourage your child to share with you the fact strategies we have used in the classroom. If your child is having trouble remembering the names of the strategies, the chart at the bottom of page 5 will help.

1 Complete these subtraction facts.

$5 - 2 =$ _3_ $8 - 3 =$ _5_ $6 - 1 =$ _5_ $9 - 2 =$ _7_

2 Complete these subtraction facts.

$12 - 6 =$ _6_ $8 - 4 =$ _4_ $16 - 8 =$ _8_ $14 - 7 =$ _7_

3 What do the facts in Problem 2 have in common?

they   all   subtract   buy   half   of

there   humber

4 Complete these subtraction facts.

9	11	12	13	12	11
-4	-4	-7	-8	-4	-5
5	7	5	5	8	6

5 Complete these subtraction facts.

$19 - 9 =$ _10_ $12 - 2 =$ _10_ $17 - 7 =$ _10_ $14 - 4 =$ _10_

6 What is the name for facts like those in Problem 5?

Subtraction

(continued on next page)

Addition & Subtraction Review page 2 of 3

7 There are 13 blue marbles and 7 red marbles in a bag. How many more blue marbles than red marbles are in the bag? Keona says this is a subtraction problem. Tamron says it is an addition problem. What do you think? Why?

Keona is right beacause if you add you will find the total number on marbles.

8 Complete these addition facts.

9	7	10	6	4	8
+ 4	+ 9	+ 8	+ 4	+ 7	+ 6
13	16	18	10	11	14

8	7	6	9	4	5
+ 3	+ 8	+ 6	+ 8	+ 7	+9
11	15	12	17	11	14

9 Complete each equation with a different pair of numbers whose difference is 6.

a _12_ – _6_ = 6   **b** _7_ – _1_ = 6

(continued on next page)

NAME | DATE

Addition & Subtraction Review page 3 of 3

10 Lisa and her dad are peeling apples to make some apple pies. The pies need 14 apples. Lisa and her dad have peeled 5 apples.

a Is there an odd or even number of apples left to peel? How do you know?

It is a odd number beacause you can not divied 9 from 2.

b How many apples are left to peel? Show your work.

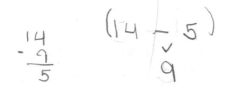

$$14 - 9 = 5$$

$$(14 - 5)$$
$$9$$

11 **CHALLENGE** Lisa has 32 clean dishes to put away after emptying the dishwasher. After she put away 4 dishes, she helped her mother bring groceries in from the car. Then she put away 7 more dishes. How many dishes still need to be put away? Show your work.

$$(32 - 4) - 7$$
$$28 - 7$$
$$21$$

Subtraction Strategy	Example
Zero facts	5 − 0 = 5, 18 − 0 = 18
Count Back facts	9 − 1 = 8, 7 − 2 = 5, 14 − 3 = 11
Take All facts	6 − 6 = 0, 15 − 15 = 0
Take Half facts	8 − 4 = 4, 12 − 6 = 6
Back to Ten facts	14 − 4 = 10, 18 − 8 = 10
Take Away Ten facts	19 − 10 = 9, 16 − 10 = 6
Up to Ten facts	For 17 − 8, start at 8, add 2 to get to 10, add 7 to get to 17. 2 + 7 = 9. 17 − 8 = 9.

🏠 Of Mice & Moles page 1 of 2

For problems 1–3, show your work using numbers, words, or labeled sketches.

1 Xavier watched a mouse walk this path. How far did the mouse travel?

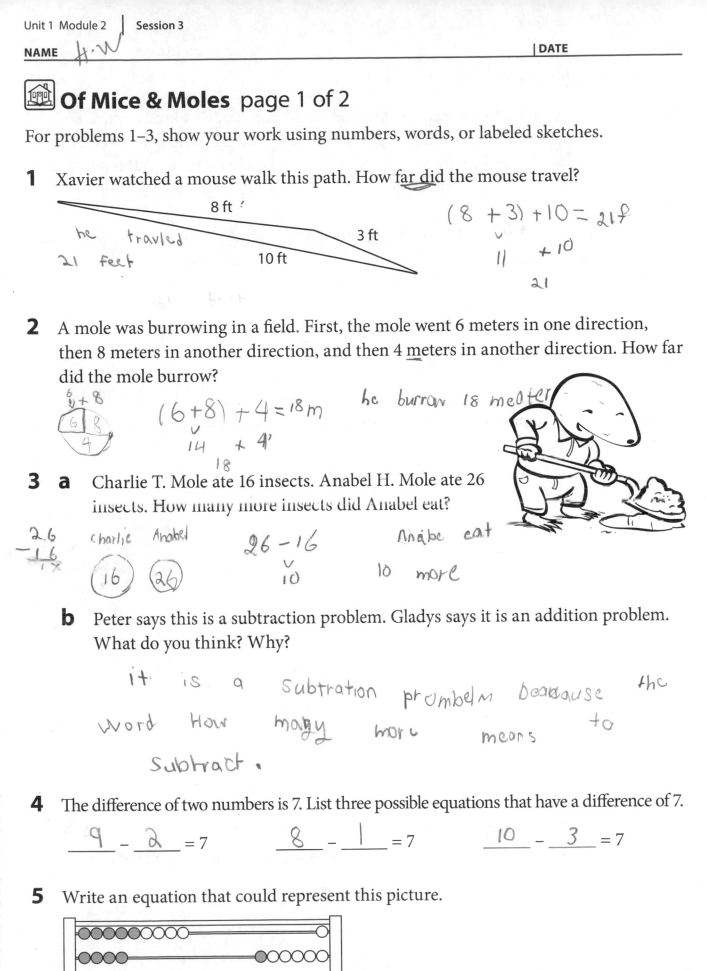

8 ft

he travled
21 feet

3 ft

10 ft

$(8 + 3) + 10 = 21f$

$11 + 10$

21

2 A mole was burrowing in a field. First, the mole went 6 meters in one direction, then 8 meters in another direction, and then 4 meters in another direction. How far did the mole burrow?

6 + 8
6 | 8
4

$(6+8) + 4 = 18m$

$14 + 4$

18

he burrow 18 melter

3 a Charlie T. Mole ate 16 insects. Anabel H. Mole ate 26 insects. How many more insects did Anabel eat?

2.6
−1.6
1 x

charlie Anabel
16 26

$26 − 16$

10

Anabe eat

10 more

b Peter says this is a subtraction problem. Gladys says it is an addition problem. What do you think? Why?

it is a subtration prumbelm becaause the word How mahy more means to subtract.

4 The difference of two numbers is 7. List three possible equations that have a difference of 7.

9 − 2 = 7   8 − 1 = 7   10 − 3 = 7

5 Write an equation that could represent this picture.

(continued on next page)

Of Mice & Moles page 2 of 2

6 **CHALLENGE** Abel S. Mouse searched for food for <u>28</u> minutes. He found a snack and spent <u>10</u> minutes eating his snack. <u>How much longer</u> did it take Abel S. Mouse to find his snack than it took him to eat it? Which of the following represents this situation?

○ $28 + s = 10$ ○ $10 + 28 = s$ ○ $38 - s = 28$ ● $28 - 10 = s$

7 Jana practiced the piano 10 minutes longer than her brother, Grant. Jana practiced for 35 minutes. How long did Grant practice? Show your work.

Jana   Grant

(35)   (25)   35 – 10   So   Grant practice

25   25 m

8 **CHALLENGE** Lulu practiced the piano for 45 minutes, and then she practiced the violin for 30 minutes.

a How much time did Lulu spend practicing her instruments? Show your work.

violin   piano   she practiced
(30) + (45)   30 + 45   75 min
75

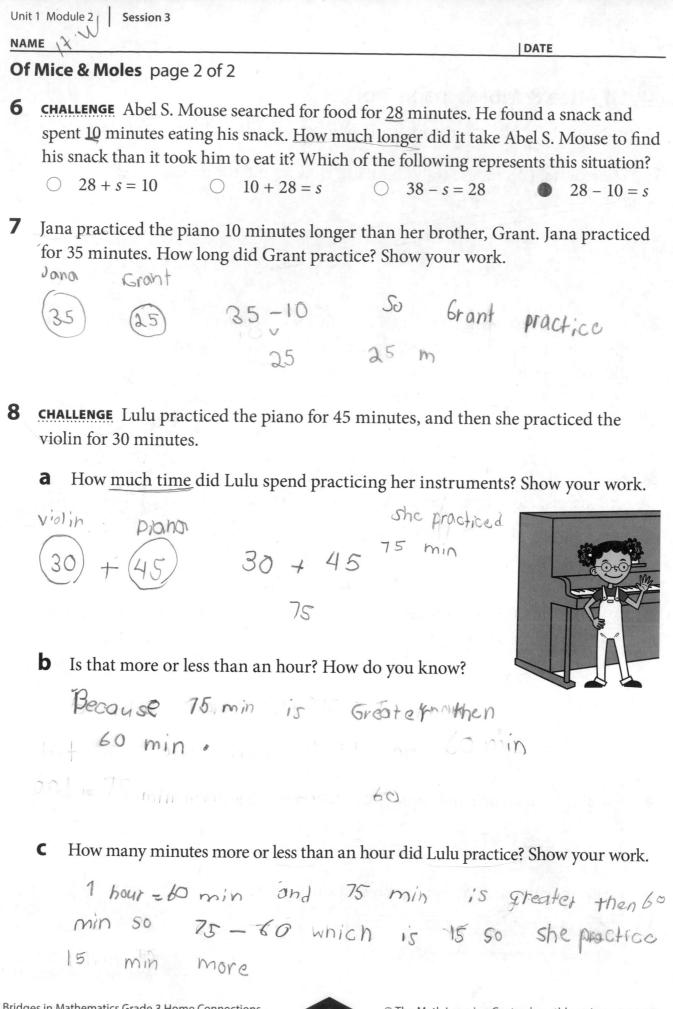

b Is that more or less than an hour? How do you know?

Because 75 min is Greater then 60 min.

c How many minutes more or less than an hour did Lulu practice? Show your work.

1 hour = 60 min and 75 min is greater then 60 min so 75 – 60 which is 15 so she practice 15 min more

1045

NAME _____ | DATE _____

Sums & Differences page 1 of 2

1 The sum of three numbers is 12. What could those three numbers be? Think of three different solutions.

12 = ____ + ____ + ____   12 = ____ + ____ + ____   12 = ____ + ____ + ____

2 The difference between two numbers is 12. What could those numbers be?

12 = _24_ – _12_   12 = _42_ – _30_   12 = _52_ – _40_

3 Look at this picture and think about the many different equations you could write to represent it.

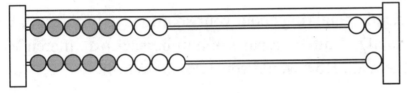

$$\begin{array}{r} 42 \\ 30 \\ \hline 12 \end{array}$$

a Write an addition equation to represent the picture above.

$$\begin{array}{r} 52 \\ 40 \\ \hline 12 \end{array}$$

b Write a subtraction equation to represent the picture above.

4 a Add each pair of numbers.

8	10	78	10	168	28	10
+ 10	+ 38	+ 10	+ 118	+ 10	+ 10	+ 58
18	48	88	128	178	38	68

b What pattern do you see in the combinations above?

(continued on next page)

Sums & Differences page 2 of 2

Use numbers, pictures, or words to show your work when you solve these problems. Use additional paper if you need more room.

5 Jack is 36 inches tall. Mary is 6 inches taller than Jack. Cameron is 4 inches taller than Mary.

a How many inches tall is Cameron?

he is 44 44 inches tall

b How many inches tall is Mary?

she is 40 inches tall

6 CHALLENGE You and your friend are talking about your solutions to problem 2. Your friend said that there are exactly 12 different pairs of numbers with a difference of 12 and that he had found them all. How would you respond to him?

This is False boacose twe can Sutract number which are greater 12

7 CHALLENGE You and your friend were thinking about pairs of whole numbers that have a *sum* of 12. How many pairs of whole numbers can you find that have a sum of 12? (Note: A whole number is equal to or greater than 0 and does not include a fraction. 2 is a whole number. 2 ½ is not a whole number.)

5+7   8+4   6+6   10+2   11+1   3+9
        12   12   12   12   12

8 CHALLENGE How many pairs of whole numbers have a sum of 40?

20+20   10+30   30+10

9 CHALLENGE How many pairs of whole numbers have a sum of 110?

45+65   64+45

10 CHALLENGE How many pairs of whole numbers have a sum of 99?

55+44   54+45   72+27

🏠 Adding Tens page 1 of 2

1 Count on by 10s to fill in the blanks below.

a 217   _227_   _237_   247   _257_   _267_   _277_   _287_   _297_

b _2_   12   _22_   _32_   42   52   _62_   _72_   _82_

c ___   ___   ___   110   ___   ___   ___   ___

d ___   ___   356   ___   376   ___   ___   ___

2 Solve each problem below. Show your work for each.

a The book measures 40 centimeters and the paper measures 120 centimeters. How long are they together if you line them up end-to-end?

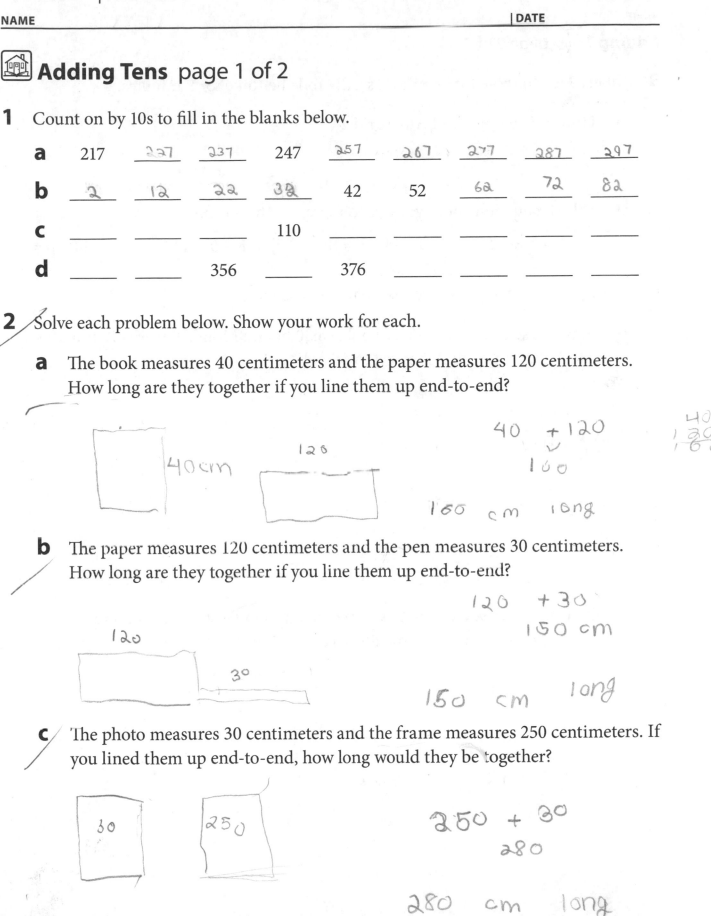

40cm   120

40 + 120
160

160 cm long

b The paper measures 120 centimeters and the pen measures 30 centimeters. How long are they together if you line them up end-to-end?

120 + 30
150 cm

120   30

150 cm long

c The photo measures 30 centimeters and the frame measures 250 centimeters. If you lined them up end-to-end, how long would they be together?

30   250

250 + 30
280

280 cm long

(continued on next page)

NAME _____ | DATE _____

Adding Tens page 2 of 2

3 Albert rode his bike for 14 minutes. Ally rode her bike for 8 minutes.

a How much longer did Albert ride?

6 min

b Which equation could you use to represent this problem:

○ $14 + 8 = b$ ○ $14 + b = 8$ ○ $8 - b = 14$ ● $14 - b = 8$

4 Show your thinking when you solve these problems:

a Bobby is supposed to be at school at 8:30 but on Monday he was 17 minutes late. What time did Bobby get to school?

8:30
8:47

BObby   reach   school

at   8:47

b **CHALLENGE** Steve was also late to school on Monday, but he got there 8 minutes before Bobby. What time did Steve get to school?

8:47
− 8
8:39

Steve   reach   school   at

8:39

H·w

🏠 More Adding Tens page 1 of 2

1 Count on by 10s to fill in the blanks below.

a   46   56   _66_   _76_   _86_   _96_   _106_   116

b   _108_   _118_   _128_   _138_   148   _158_   _168_   _178_

c   _202_   _212_   _222_   232   _242_   _252_   _262_   _272_

d   ____   ____   756   ____   776   ____   ____   ____

2 Solve the problems below. Show your work for each.

a The book measures 45 units and the paper measures 23 units. How long are they together if you line them up?

45 + 23
65 units long

[45] [23]

42
+23
65

b The pencil measures 20 units and the pen measures 32 units. How long are they together if you line them up?

20 + 32

52 units long

[20] [32]

c The photo measures 95 units and the frame measures 25 units. If you lined them up, how long would they be together?

[95] [25]

95 + 25
120 units long

95
25
120

d You line up a paper, pencil, and pen and they measure 43 units end to end. The paper measures 23 units, the pencil measures 10 units. What does the pen measure?

+23
10
43

43 - 23 + 10
20 - 10
10

the anwser is
10

(continued on next page)

More Adding Tens page 2 of 2

3 Alex's goal this month is to ride 20 miles on his bike. One week he rode 5 miles, the next week he rode 6 miles, and this past week he rode 8 miles.

a How many miles has Alex ridden so far?

5 + 6 + 8   19 miles

b How many miles does Alex still need to ride to meet his goal of riding 20 miles this month?

1   miles   more

4 Alex's sister Hazel also likes to bicycle a lot. In three weeks, she rode a total of 20 miles. How many miles did she ride each week? Find at least four solutions to the problem.

Week 1	Week 2	Week 3	Total
8	2	10	= 20 miles
6	4	10	= 20 miles
7	3	10	= 20 miles
9	1	10	= 20 miles

5 Steve and Henry rode their bikes completely around Brightwood Park. The distances are marked on the map. How many kilometers (km) did they ride? Show your work.

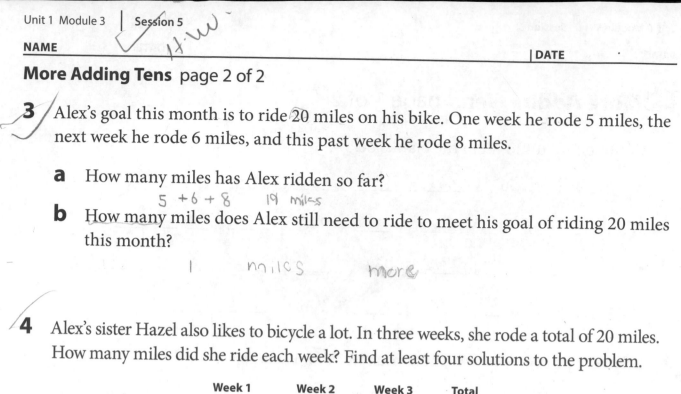

13 km
Brightwood Park
4 km
8 km
12 km

13 + 8 + 12 + 4
21 + 16
37 km

6 Logan's dog, Chief, likes to patrol along the fence of Logan's backyard to make sure everything is as it should be. How many feet does Chief walk every time he patrols the yard? Show your work.

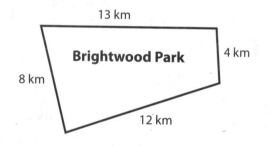

60 ft
40 ft   Logan's yard   40 ft
60 ft

(60 + 60) + (40 + 40)
120   +   80
200 ft

 **Making Ten** page 1 of 2

1 Complete each equation.

$7 +$ __3__ $= 10$ $10 = 2 +$ __8__   __5__ $+ 5 = 10$ $10 =$ __4__ $+ 6$

2 Complete each equation.

$27 +$ __3__ $= 30$ $30 = 2 +$ __28__   __25__ $+ 5 = 30$ $30 =$ __4__ $+ 26$

$27 +$ __13__ $= 40$ $40 = 2 +$ __38__   __35__ $+ 5 = 40$ $40 =$ __14__ $+ 26$

$27 +$ __53__ $= 80$ $80 = 2 +$ __78__   __75__ $+ 5 = 80$ $80 =$ __54__ $+ 26$

3 Show your thinking when you solve these problems.

a Fiona's team had 27 points and the other team had 40 points. The team with the most points wins the game. If the other team scored no more points, how many more points would Fiona's team need to win?

41   points   beacousc   they   nccd

morc   than   the   other   tcam   to

win.

b Mark has $35. He needs $80 to buy the bike he really wants. How much more money does Mark need to buy the bike?

$$
\begin{array}{r}
7\ 10 \\
8\ 8\!\!\!\!\diagdown\ 0 \\
-\ 35 \\
\hline
45
\end{array}
$$

hc   will   nccd   45 $ dollrs

morc   bcaeaus $80 - 35 = 40$

(continued on next page)

NAME _____ | DATE _____

Making Ten page 2 of 2

4 Show your thinking when you solve these problems.

a Terilyn and Mark are on a fishing trip. Terilyn caught 13 fish. She has to catch 10 more to have as many fish as Mark. How many fish has Mark caught?

$$+\ \begin{array}{r} 13 \\ 10 \\ \hline 23 \end{array}$$

She will need to catch
23 because 13 + 10 = 23

b Terilyn has some grapes in her lunch. She gave 20 grapes to Mark, and now she has 28 grapes left. How many grapes did Terilyn have to start with?

$$\begin{array}{r} 20 \\ 28 \\ \hline 48 \end{array}$$

She started with 48
leves because 20 + 28 = 40

Double-Digit Addition page 1 of 2

1 Add each pair of numbers. Show all your work. Try to use different methods to add the numbers.

a $20 + 20 =$	**b** $40 + 30 =$	**c** $30 + 60 =$
20 20 + 20 20 40	40 40 + 30 30 70	3 + 6 + 00 80
d 50 + 80 5 + 8 111 140	**e** 70 + 80 150	**f** 90 + 20 110

2 Victor had 120 baseball cards. His cousin gave him 40 more cards. Then his brother gave him 50 more cards. How many baseball cards does Victor have now? Show all your work.

$120 + 40 + 50$

1.60
50
210

160 + 50

210

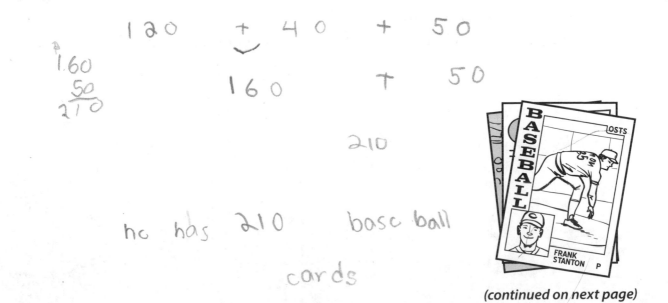

he has 210 base ball cards

(continued on next page)

Double-Digit Addition page 2 of 2

Show all your work when you solve these problems.

3 The toy store is having a special on board games. If you buy two games for $17 each, you get $5 off the total. How much would you end up paying for those two games?

(17 + 17) - 5

34 - 5

29

thcy paid 29 $

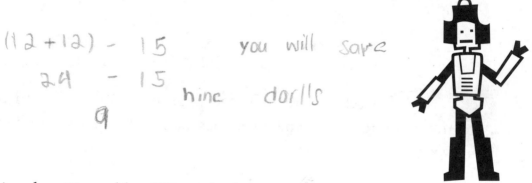

4 Action figures that usually cost $12 are on sale. During the sale you can get two action figures for $15. How much do you save when you buy two for $15?

(12 + 12) - 15   you will save

24 - 15   hine dorlls

9

5 **CHALLENGE** Jaime has 38 marbles. If Jorge had 14 more marbles, he would have twice as many marbles as Jaime. How many marbles does Jorge have now?

76
14
62

38
2
76

(38 x 2) ÷ 14

76 - 14

Jorge has 62 marbles

Patterns & Sums page 1 of 2

1 Add each pair of numbers. Show all your work.

a 30 + 65 = 85 30 65 85	**b** 42 + 35 = 77 42 35 77	**c** 46 + 38 = 84 48 38 84
d 53 + 82 135	**e** 67 + 85 152	**f** 94 + 76 170

2 Victor had 126 Lego pieces. His cousin gave him 20 more Lego pieces. Then his brother gave him 58 more. How many Lego pieces does Victor have now? Show all your work.

126   +   20   + 58

146   +   58

146
 58
 204

204   180

(continued on next page)

NAME _____ | DATE _____

Patterns & Sums page 2 of 2

Show your work when solving these story problems.

3 Some of the third graders and fourth graders started a new kickball game at recess. The third graders scored 8 runs in the first inning and 4 runs in the second inning. The fourth graders scored 5 runs in the first inning and 16 runs in the second. How many more runs do the fourth graders have?

$(16 + 5) - (18 + 4)$

$21 - 12$

9 runs more

$\begin{array}{r} 21 \\ -12 \\ \hline 09 \end{array}$

4 **CHALLENGE** Barbara has three chickens. Last week they each laid 4 eggs, and this week they each laid 5 eggs. Barbara gave 8 eggs away and used 7 of the eggs for making breakfasts and cookies. How many eggs does she have left?

$(3 \times 4) + (3 \times 5) = 8 \quad -7$

$12 + 15$

$27 - 8 - 7$

$19 - 7$

12

she has 12 egg left

🏠 The Pet Store   page 1 of 2

Note to Family

At school, we have started looking for efficient ways to find the total number of items in a group. We studied a picture of a pet store that was full of packages and containers. We worked to figure out how many items were in each package and then how many were in all the packages together. Sometimes, the arrangement of items was helpful—for example, a package of cat food had 2 rows of cans with 5 cans in each one. This made it easier to count by 2s or 5s to find the total. Watch how your child makes use of each of the arrangements in this assignment to help find the total.

Use the pictures to find the total for each problem below. Show your thinking with numbers, sketches, or words.

ex How many cans of dog food are there? How do you know?

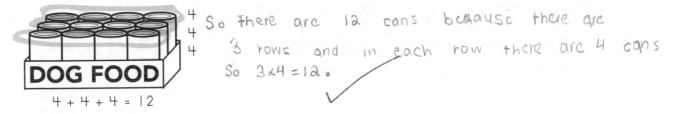

4
4
4

So there are 12 cans because there are 3 rows and in each row there are 4 cans So 3×4 =12. ✓

4 + 4 + 4 = 12

1 How many cans of cat food are there? How do you know?

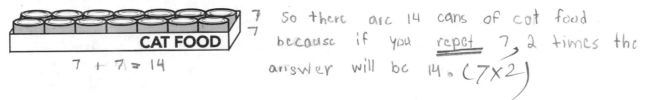

7
7

So there are 14 cans of cat food because if you repet 7, 2 times the answer will be 14. (7×2)

7 + 7 = 14

2 How many balls are there in all? How do you know?

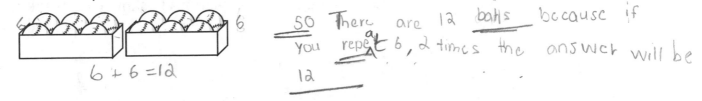

6

SO There are 12 balls because if you repet 6, 2 times the answer will be 12

6 + 6 = 12

3 How many chew toys are there? How do you know?

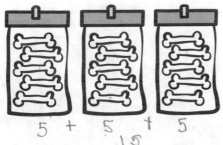

So There are 15 chew toys because 5+5+5 or 5×3 = 15.

5 + 5 + 5
15

(continued on next page)

NAME _____ | DATE _____

The Pet Store page 2 of 2

4 Fill in the blanks.

17 – 8 = _9_   6 + 7 = _13_   13 – 9 = _4_

3 + _7_ = 10   16 – _8_ = 8   5 + _10_ = 15

4 + 4 + 4 + 4 = _16_   8 + 8 + 8 = _24_   6 + 6 + 6 = _18_

5 **CHALLENGE** Molly's kitten weighed 3 pounds when she got her. Now the kitten has gained 4 pounds, and Molly's dog weighs 4 times as much as her kitten.

a How many pounds does the kitten weigh now?
Write equations to show your thinking.

3 + 4 = 7 pounds   (So) I think if the kat
weighed 3 pounds and now it
gained 4 pounds so the kitten
would weight 7 pounds because
3 + 4 = 7 pounds

b How many pounds does the dog weigh? Write equations to show your thinking.

(3 + 4) × 4 = 28 pounds   So I think the
7 × 4   dog weight 28 p because
28   7 × 4 = 28.

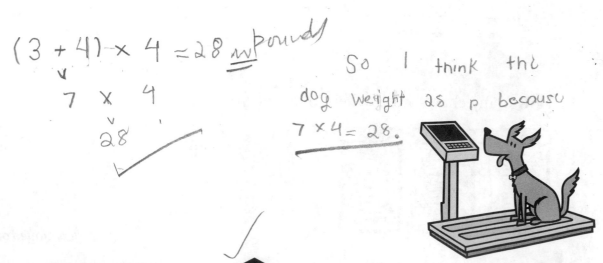

NAME _____ | DATE _____

🏠 Stamp Challenges page 1 of 2

Use the images to find the total for each problem below. Show your thinking with numbers, sketches, or words.

ex How many stamps do you see? What is the total cost of the stamps?

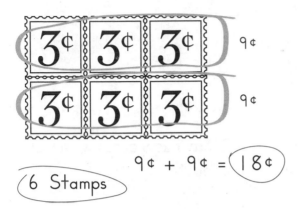

9¢

9¢

9¢ + 9¢ = (18¢)

(6 Stamps)

1 How many stamps do you see? What is the total cost of the stamps?

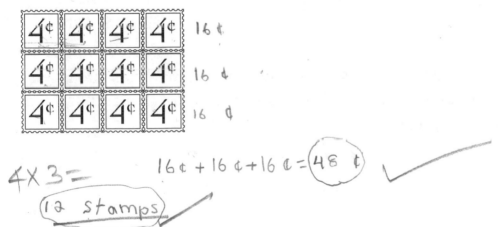

16¢

16¢

16¢

4 X 3 =

(12 stamps)

16¢ + 16¢ + 16¢ = (48¢) ✓

2 How many stamps do you see? What is the total cost of the stamps?

15¢

15¢

15¢ + 15¢ = (¢ 30)

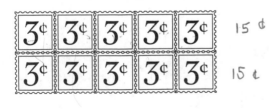

(10 stamp)

(continued on next page)

Stamp Challenges page 2 of 2

3 How many stamps do you see? What is the total cost of the stamps?

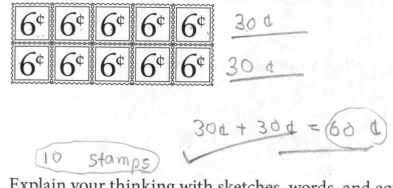

30¢

30¢

30¢ + 30¢ = 60¢

10 stamps

4 Explain your thinking with sketches, words, and equations.

a Stevie has 4 cards with 8 stamps on each card. Cindy has 8 cards with 4 stamps on each card. Who has more stamps, Stevie or Cindy?

Stevie

4 × 8 = 32 s

32

Cindy

8 × 4 =

32

Stevie and Cindy have the same amount of stmaps beacous 8×4 = 4×8.

b **CHALLENGE** Liz bought sixteen 3¢ stamps and used them to mail two letters to her grandparents. If each letter used the same number of stamps, how much did it cost to mail each letter?

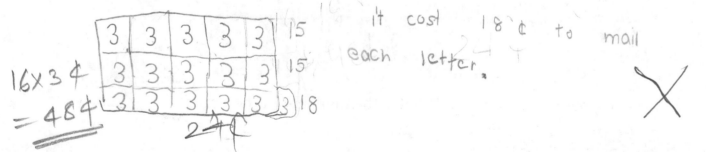

16 × 3¢ = 48¢

| 3 | 3 | 3 | 3 | 3 | 15
| 3 | 3 | 3 | 3 | 3 | 15
| 3 | 3 | 3 | 3 | 3 | 3 | 18

24¢

It cost 18¢ to mail each letter.

c **CHALLENGE** Create a new set of stamps. Decide how many stamps you want in the array and how much each stamp costs. (They should all cost the same amount.) Then find the total cost of the stamps.

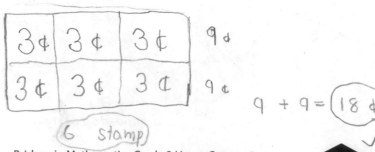

| 3¢ | 3¢ | 3¢ | 9¢
| 3¢ | 3¢ | 3¢ | 9¢

9 + 9 = 18¢

6 stamp

🏠 Leaves & Flower Petals page 1 of 2

Answer each question below. Write an addition or multiplication equation to show how you figured it out.

Answer the question.	Write an equation.
ex There are 3 flowers. How many *leaves?* 6	$2 + 2 + 2 = 6$ or $3 \times 2 = 6$
1 There are 3 flowers. How many *petals?* 6	$2 + 2 + 2 = 6$ or $3 \times 2 = 6$ 5×3
2 There are 7 flowers. How many *leaves?* 14	$2+2+2+2+2+2+2 = 14$ $7+7=$ or $2 \times 7 = 14$
3 There are 4 flowers. How many *petals?* 8	$2 + 2 + 2 + 2 = 8$ or $2 \times 4 = 8$

(continued on next page)

NAME _____ | DATE _____

Leaves & Flower Petals page 2 of 2

Complete the following problems. Show your work using numbers, sketches, or words.

4 Mrs. Foley picked 27 flowers from her garden so her 3 children could each give a bouquet to their teachers. If each bouquet had the same number of flowers, how many flowers did each teacher get?

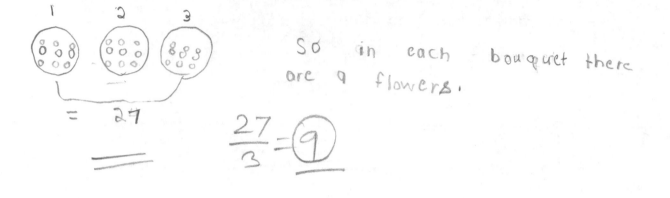

So in each bouquet there are 9 flowers.

$$\frac{27}{3} = 9$$

5 Which equation describes the situation in problem 4 above?

○ $27 + 3 = n$ ● $3 \times n = 27$ ○ $n + 3 = 27$ ○ $27 \times 3 = n$

6 **CHALLENGE** Terry had 14 tulips and twice as many daffodils. How many flowers did Terry have in all?

\# of Daffodils = 14 × 2 (14 + 14) = 28

(14 + 14) + 14   So he has 42 flower altogether.

28 + 14

42 f

🏠 Skip-Counting & More page 1 of 2

1 Skip-count forward from each number. A few of the numbers have been filled in for you.

3	6	9	12	15	18	21	24	27

4	8	12	16	20	24	28	32	36

5	10	15	20	25	30	35	40	45

2 a Solve the following problems.

$2 \times 10 = $ __20__ $4 \times 10 = $ __40__ $8 \times 10 = $ __80__

b What do you notice about these problems?

that ie you add to 20 to each onswer it will tell you ther next anwser

3 a Solve the following problems.

$4 \times 6 = $ __24__ $3 \times 8 = $ __24__ $2 \times 12 = $ __24__

b What do you notice about these problems?

that all of the problems = 24

(continued on next page)

Skip Counting & More page 2 of 2

4 Solve the following problems. Show your thinking using equations, sketches, or words.

a The greater roadrunner bird can run <u>14 miles per hour</u>. That's 7 times faster than an ostrich can walk. How <u>fast</u> does an ostrich walk?

$$7\overline{)14}$$ with quotient 2, -14, remainder $\times\times$

the ostrich ~~can~~ walks 2 miles per hour.

b **CHALLENGE** The body of a greater roadrunner is 16 inches long. Its tail is another 8 inches. The total length of a greater roadrunner is 4 times longer than a lovebird. How many inches long is the lovebird?

$$(16 + 8) \div 4 = 6 \text{ in}$$

24

$$24 \div 4$$

6

The lovebird is 6 <u>inches</u> long.

© The Math Learning Center | mathlearningcenter.org

NAME _____ | DATE _____

🏠 Story Problems & Number Line Puzzles page 1 of 2

Story Problems

1 Solve each problem. Use pictures, numbers, or words to show your thinking. Then write an equation for the problem.

a Roza is 4 years old. Her sister Elsa is <u>twice</u> as old as Roza. How old is Elsa?

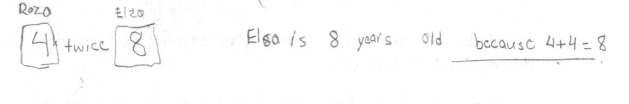

Roza [4] twice Elsa [8]   Elsa is 8 years old because 4+4 = 8

Equation: ____4+4 = 8____ ✓

b Theo's baby brother, Thomas, is 24 inches tall. Theo is <u>twice</u> as tall as Thomas. How tall is Theo?

baby brother [24] twice thomas [48]   Thomas is 48 inches tall.

Equation: ____24 + 24 = 48____ ✓

c Savannah has read 4 pages in her new book. Carlos has read 4 times as many pages as Savannah. How many pages has Carlos read?

Savannah [4 pages] x4 Carlos [16]   So carlos read 16 pages

4 x 4 = 16

Equation: ____4 x 4 = 16____

(continued on next page)

NAME _____ | **DATE** _____

Story Problems & Number Line Puzzles page 2 of 2

Number Line Puzzles

2 Here is a number line puzzle. Use what you know about multiplication to fill in the blanks.

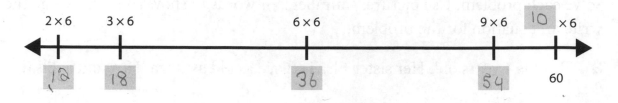

2 × 6   3 × 6   6 × 6   9 × 6   10 × 6

12   18   36   54   60

3 Use pictures, numbers, and words to solve the problem. Then select the equations that represent the problem.

a Tim saw some monkeys sitting in trees at the zoo. There were 6 monkeys sitting in each tree. There were 24 monkeys in all. How many trees were there?

There are 6 tress
In all.

b Which two equations describe the situation in problem 3a?

○ 24 + 6 = n   ○ 6 × n = 24   ○ 24 − 6 = n   ● 24 ÷ 6 = n

4 **CHALLENGE** The Turner family went bike camping at a state park near their city. It took them 4 hours of riding to get there from their house. For the first 2 hours they rode 12 miles per hour. For the last 2 hours they rode 9 miles per hour. How far is the state park campground from their house?

(12 + 12) + (9 + 9) =

24 + 18

42

The state park is 24 miles from their house

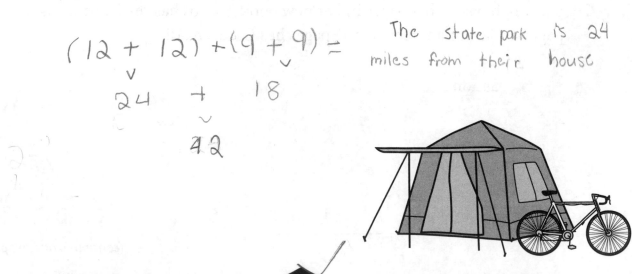

NAME _____ | **DATE** _____

🏠 More Windows page 1 of 2

1 Figure out how many windowpanes are in each window. Show your thinking with words, numbers, and pictures. Write an equation for each problem.

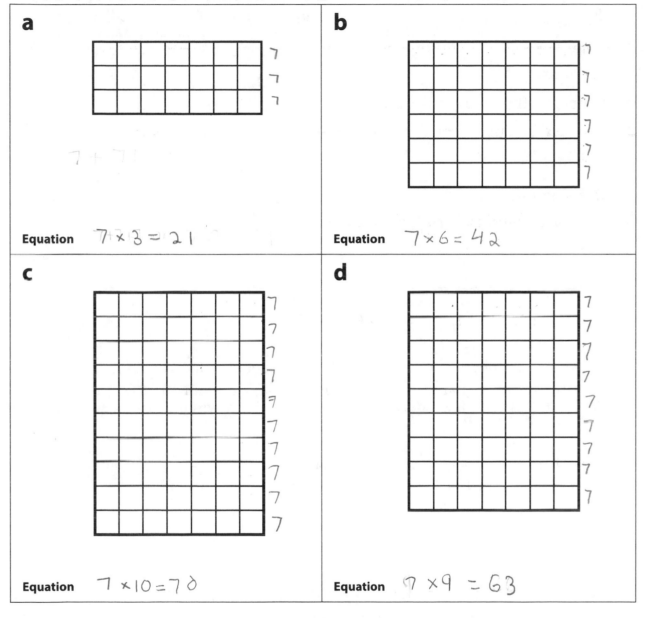

a

Equation $7 \times 3 = 21$

b

Equation $7 \times 6 = 42$

c

Equation $7 \times 10 = 70$

d

Equation $7 \times 9 = 63$

2 Solve each equation below.

$\underline{6} \times 4 = 24$ $8 \times \underline{3} = 24$ $6 \times 4 = \underline{24}$

$10 \times \underline{4} = 40$ $5 \times 8 = \underline{40}$ $\underline{8} \times 5 = 40$

$3 \times 9 = \underline{27}$ $9 \times \underline{3} = 27$ $\underline{9} \times 3 = 27$

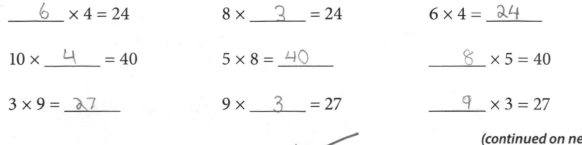

(continued on next page)

NAME _____ | **DATE** _____

More Windows page 2 of 2

3 Fill in the blanks in the skip-counts below.

a

4	8	12	16	20	24	28	32	36	40

b

6	12	18	24	30	36	42	48	54	60

4 Complete the problems below.

$2 \times 3 = \underline{6}$ $4 \times 3 = \underline{12}$ $8 \times 3 = \underline{24}$ $10 \times 3 = \underline{30}$ $9 \times 3 = \underline{27}$

5 Complete the Number Line Puzzle below.

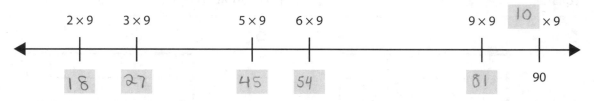

6 Solve each problem. Show your thinking with equations, sketches, or words.

a Carl can wash 8 windows in an hour. How many windows can he wash in 3 hours?

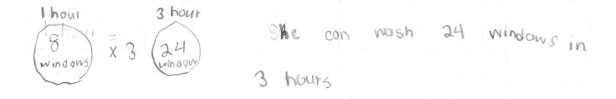

She can wash 24 windows in 3 hours

b **CHALLENGE** Sarah can wash 7 windows in an hour. Lilja can wash 4 windows in an hour. How many windows can Sarah and Lilja wash in 4 hours if they work together?

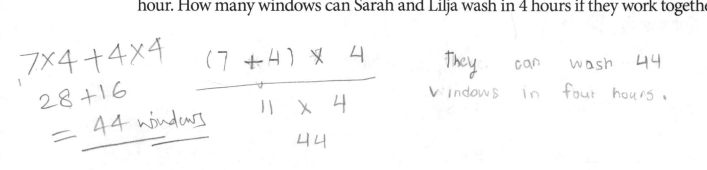

$7 \times 4 + 4 \times 4$

$28 + 16$

$= \underline{44 \text{ windows}}$

$(7 + 4) \times 4$

11×4

44

They can wash 44 windows in four hours.

NAME _____ | DATE _____

🏠 Mixed Practice page 1 of 2

Number Puzzles

1 Find the missing numbers in the equations below.

$5 \times$ __4__ $= 20$ __8__ $\times 3 = 24$ $9 \times 3 =$ __27__

$4 +$ __10__ $= 14$ $18 -$ __9__ $= 9$ __15__ $- 7 = 8$

$4 \times$ __7__ $= 28$ $8 \times 4 =$ __32__   __6__ $\times 6 = 36$

$16 -$ __7__ $= 9$ __5__ $+ 8 = 13$ $9 +$ __3__ $= 12$

$8 \times 2 =$ __16__ $7 \times$ __5__ $= 35$ __4__ $\times 3 = 12$

2 Are the following true or false? Why?

a $9 + 5 = 10 + 4$ (True) False   Explain: because   14 and 14 are   equal

b $9 - 5 = 10 - 4$ True (False)   Explain: because   6   is   greater then 4

c $9 \times 5 = 10 \times 4$ True (False)   Explain: because   45 is   greater then 40

Solve each problem. Show your thinking with equations, sketches, or words.

3 Suzie studies multiplication fact cards at home every Monday through Friday for 7 minutes on each of those days. How many minutes does she study the multiplication facts in a week?

$\begin{array}{r} 7 \\ \times\ 7 \\ \hline 49 \end{array}$ so   she   study   49   min

4 Jim paid $48 to buy a package of 6 flea treatments for his dog. How much does one flea treatment cost?

each   flea   treament   cost

8 $ doller

(continued on next page)

NAME _____ | **DATE** _____

Mixed Practice page 2 of 2

5 **CHALLENGE** Each flea treatment usually lasts for about 4 weeks, but one year the fleas were especially bad. Jim's dog needed to be treated for fleas every 3 weeks until the weather cooled off.

a How many weeks of flea treatments would Jim's dog get from one package if each treatment only lasted 3 weeks?

he will need 18 treats in 3 weeks

b In a normal year, when a flea treatment lasts 4 weeks, how many more weeks of treatments would Jim's dog get from one package?

he will need 6 more flex terment

6 **CHALLENGE** Bobby's favorite cupcakes come in packages of 4. He asked his grandma to buy them for a class party. She had to go to two grocery stores to get enough cupcakes for all the kids in the class. She bought 5 packages at the first store and 2 packages at the second store. How many cupcakes did Bobby's grandmother buy in all?

$$(4 \times 5) + (2 \times 4)$$
$$20 + 8$$
$$28$$

So bobby grandpa

brought 28 cupcake in all.

NAME _____ | DATE _____

 **Grocery Shopping** page 1 of 2

1 Fill in the tables below.

Grapes $3.00 per pound	
Number of Pounds	Cost
1	$3.00
2	
4	
	$15.00
10	
20	

Potatoes $1.25 per pound	
Number of Pounds	Cost
1	$1.25
2	
4	
	$6.25
10	
12	

Missing Numbers

2 Find the missing numbers in the equations below.

$3 \times$ _____ $= 12$ _____ $\times 3 = 18$ $7 \times 3 =$ _____

$5 \times$ _____ $= 25$ $7 \times 4 =$ _____   _____ $\times 6 = 30$

$6 \times 4 =$ _____ $6 \times$ _____ $= 36$ _____ $\times 2 = 12$

(continued on next page)

   35

NAME | **DATE**

Grocery Shopping page 2 of 2

3 Solve each problem. Show your thinking with equations, sketches, or words.

a A 10-pack of instant oatmeal costs $2.00. How much does each pack cost?

so each pack cost 20 ¢

$$\begin{array}{r} \times\ 20 \\ 10 \\ \hline 00 \\ 200 \\ \hline 200 \end{array}$$

b **CHALLENGE** Oranges are 2 pounds for $1.00. Apples are $2.00 per pound. Chris bought 5 pounds of oranges and 3 pounds of apples. How much did Chris pay for all the fruit?

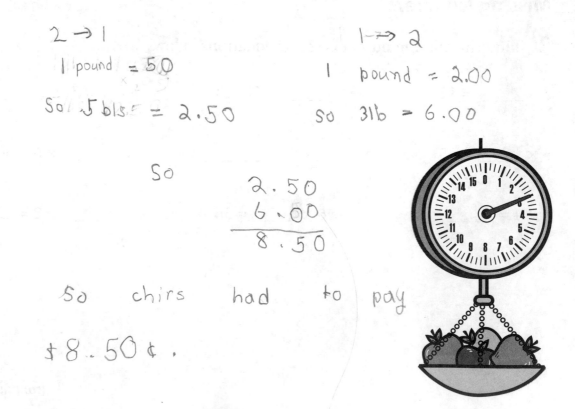

2 → 1   1 → 2
1 pound = 50   1 pound = 2.00
So 5 bls = 2.50   so 3lb = 6.00

So   2.50
             6.00
           ‾‾‾‾‾‾
             8.50

So chirs had to pay

$8.50 ¢.

 **Favorite Pets** page 1 of 2

1 Look at the two graphs below and then answer the following questions.

a Do the picture graph and the bar graph above represent the same data?

Yes

b Why or why not?

Yes because the number and the data is same

c Using the picture graph, tell how many students are in the class. Explain how you know.

In-

d Using the bar graph, tell how many students are in the class. Explain how you know.

19 because if add all of the number

2 **CHALLENGE** Mr. Neon's class took a survey to find out everyone's favorite fruit. The number of votes for each fruit is listed below. On a separate sheet of paper, draw a picture graph that shows the information. Be sure your graph has a title and labels.

Bananas: 3   Apples: 7   Grapes: 6   Watermelon: 4   Strawberries: 4

(continued on next page)

Favorite Pets page 2 of 2

Review

3 Conrad says that 8 × 7 is the same as 8 × 5 plus 8 × 2. Do you agree or disagree? Explain your thinking.

I disargce beacaues 8 × 7 = 56
and 8 × 5 + 8 × 2 is 61
and 61 is grcather 56

4 Alexis says that 6 × 9 is the same as 6 × 9 plus 6 × 9. Do you agree or disagree? Explain your thinking.

I disagrci because 108 is grcathe
then 54

5 CHALLENGE Melea needs to provide 200 pieces of fruit for the local elementary school. Melea has 15 baskets. Each basket has 9 pieces of fruit in it. Does Melea have enough fruit? Show your thinking with numbers, pictures, or words.

🏠 The Pencil Survey page 1 of 2

One day last spring, Ms. Brown asked her third graders to clean out their desks. She couldn't believe how many pencils most of the kids pulled out. "So that's where all the pencils have been!" she thought.

Ms. Brown decided to take a survey to find out how many pencils had been hiding in the kids' desks. The table below shows the survey results.

Number of Pencils	Number of Students
1	2
2	7
3	8
4	5
7	3
8	2
10	1
12	1

1 a Record the data on the line plot below.

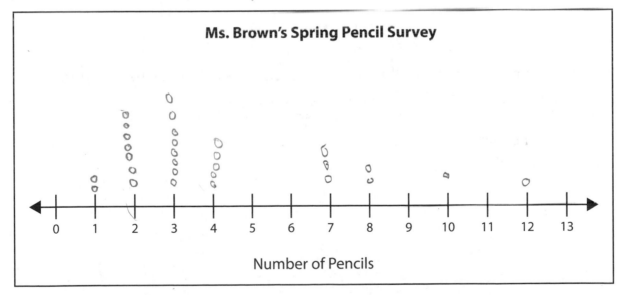

Ms. Brown's Spring Pencil Survey

Number of Pencils

b What was the most common number of pencils for a student to have in their desk in the spring?

number 3

(continued on next page)

NAME _____ | DATE _____

The Pencil Survey page 2 of 2

2 a The next year, Ms. Brown thought, "I will ask the students to clean out their desks earlier this year so we don't run out of pencils so fast." The line plot below shows how many pencils the kids found in their desks that time.

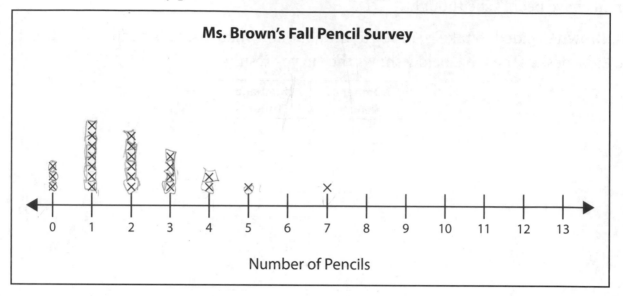

Ms. Brown's Fall Pencil Survey

Number of Pencils

b What was the most common number of pencils for a student to have in their desk in the fall?

number   1

3 Were there more pencils hiding in the students' desks last spring (see problem 1) or in the fall (see problem 2)? Explain how you figured it out.

they was more last spring because when I add the pencil the ansew 29 but the answer for fall was 24. and 29 is greater then 24

4 **CHALLENGE** Exactly how many pencils were hiding in students' desks when Ms. Brown did the fall survey? (Hint: Be careful! The answer is not 24 pencils.)

 they found 22 pencils

Multiplying & Dividing page 1 of 2

1 Complete the multiplication facts.

5	2	1	5	3	8	5
×6	×7	×2	×7	×5	×5	×9

4	5	9	2	10	10	4
×2	×2	×2	×5	×3	×5	×6

10	1	2	7	6	10	3
×0	×8	×3	×4	×6	×8	×9

2 Complete the division facts.

$100 \div 10 =$ __10__ $16 \div 2 =$ __8__ $25 \div 5 =$ __5__

$12 \div 2 -$ __6__ $3 \div 1 =$ __3__ $20 \div 2 =$ __10__

3 **CHALLENGE** Use what you know about basic fact strategies to solve these multiplication problems.

24	42	329	13	1,946	500	25
× 5	× 5	× 0	× 10	× 1	× 2	× 6
120	210	000	00	1946	1000	150
			13			
			130			

4 **a** Would the product of 3,407 × 10 be odd or even? __even__

b How do you know?

beacaus   I did mutiply on

a   staped   piccs   of   paper

(continued on next page)

NAME _____ *cheack complite* | DATE _____

Multiplying & Dividing page 2 of 2

5 Will is helping his mom get ready for a party. His mom wants Will to put flowers in jars to put on the tables. He needs to put 7 flowers in each jar. He has 45 flowers.

a How many jars can he fill? Show all your work.

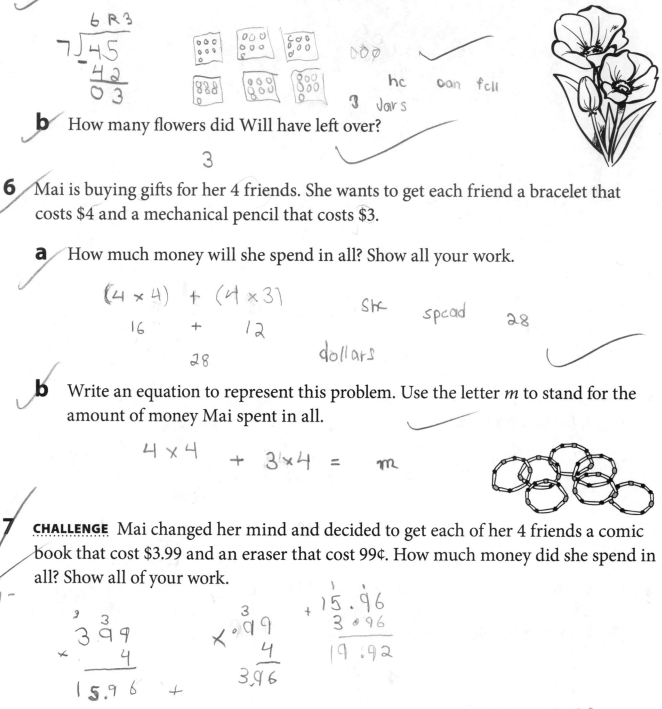

6 R 3

7⟌45
  42
  0 3

he can fell
3 Jars

b How many flowers did Will have left over?

3

6 Mai is buying gifts for her 4 friends. She wants to get each friend a bracelet that costs $4 and a mechanical pencil that costs $3.

a How much money will she spend in all? Show all your work.

$(4 \times 4) + (4 \times 3)$

16 + 12

28

She spead 28 dollars

b Write an equation to represent this problem. Use the letter *m* to stand for the amount of money Mai spent in all.

$4 \times 4 + 3 \times 4 = m$

7 **CHALLENGE** Mai changed her mind and decided to get each of her 4 friends a comic book that cost $3.99 and an eraser that cost 99¢. How much money did she spend in all? Show all of your work.

3.99
× 4
15.96 +

0.99
× 4
3.96

15.96
+ 3.96
19.92

She spead 19.92

NAME _____ | DATE _____

🏠 Rounding to the Nearest Ten page 1 of 2

You can use a number line to help round to the nearest ten. If a number is closer to the next larger multiple of 10, round up. If it is closer to the next smaller multiple of 10, round down.

If the digit in the ones place is 5 or higher, round up. If the digit in the ones place is less than 5, round down.

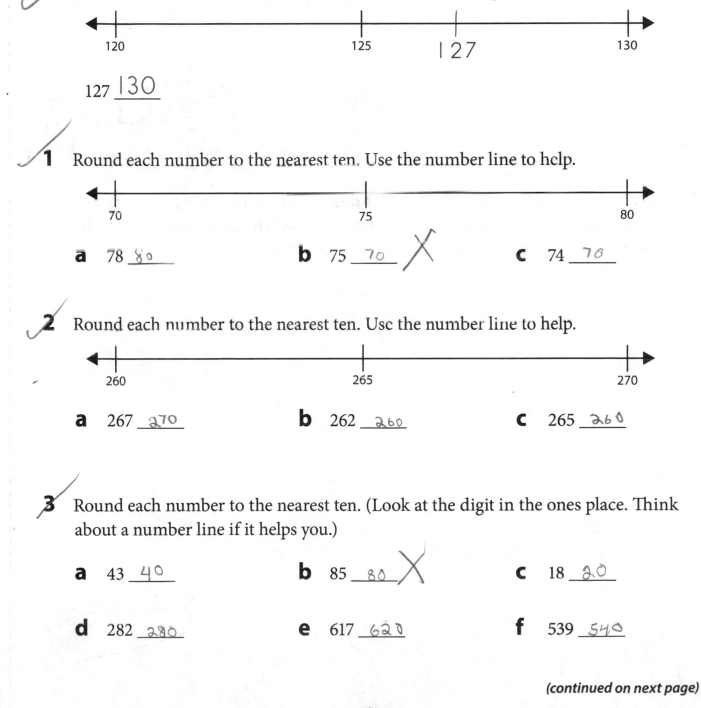

ex Round 127 to the nearest ten. Use the number line to help.

127 _130_

1 Round each number to the nearest ten. Use the number line to help.

a 78 _80_   **b** 75 _70_ ✗   **c** 74 _70_

2 Round each number to the nearest ten. Use the number line to help.

a 267 _270_   **b** 262 _260_   **c** 265 _260_

3 Round each number to the nearest ten. (Look at the digit in the ones place. Think about a number line if it helps you.)

a 43 _40_   **b** 85 _80_ ✗   **c** 18 _20_

d 282 _280_   **e** 617 _620_   **f** 539 _540_

(continued on next page)

NAME | **DATE**

Rounding to the Nearest Ten page 2 of 2

4 The third and fourth graders at Fernwood School are going on a field trip. They will fill 3 school buses. Each bus holds 52 passengers. How many people will be going on the field trip? Show your work.

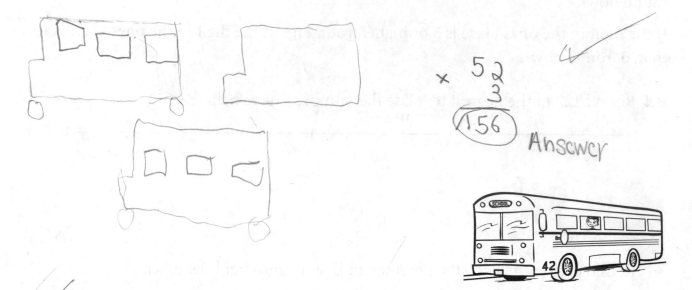

$$\times \begin{array}{r} 52 \\ 3 \end{array}$$

156 ✓

Answer

5 **CHALLENGE** Mr. Kelly bought 8 dozen hot dogs for the third grade picnic. His pet dog broke into the groceries and ate 14 hot dogs. If each picnic guest eats one hot dog, how many people can still have a hot dog? Show your work.

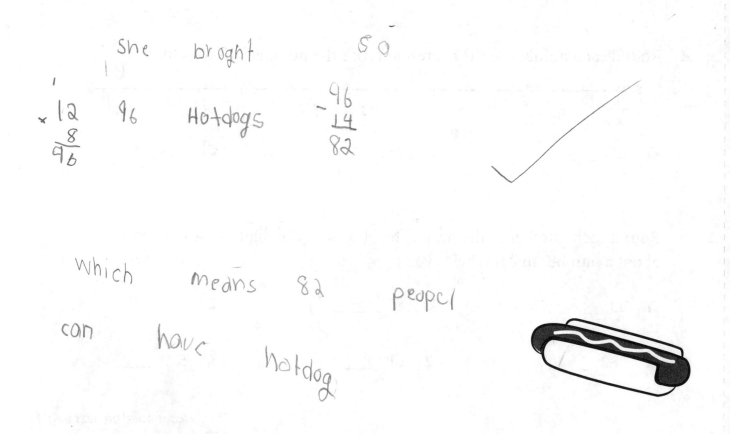

She brought 60

$\times \begin{array}{r} 12 \\ 8 \\ \hline 96 \end{array}$ 96 Hotdogs $\begin{array}{r} 96 \\ -14 \\ \hline 82 \end{array}$

Which means 82 peopel can have hotdog

NAME _____ | DATE _____

🏠 Round & Round page 1 of 2

1 Rounding numbers can help you make good estimates. Round each pair of numbers to the nearest ten and then add the rounded numbers to estimate the sum.

Numbers to Add	Rounded to the Nearest Ten	Estimated Sum
ex 237 + 349	240 + 350	240 + 350 590

The sum of 237 and 349 is about equal to __590__ .

Numbers to Add	Rounded to the Nearest Ten	Estimated Sum
a 168 + 122	170 + 120	170 + 120 290

The sum of 168 and 122 is about equal to __290__ .

Numbers to Add	Rounded to the Nearest Ten	Estimated Sum
b 147 + 618	150 + 620	147 + 618 765 X

The sum of 147 and 618 is about equal to __765__ . X

2 Estimate for each story problem below. Explain your estimation using numbers, sketches, or words.

a Ravi likes to ride on the merry-go-round. Each ride lasts for 49 seconds. If Ravi takes 2 rides, about how long does he spend on the merry-go-round?

49   49
49 or × 2   So he spends 98 seconds
98   98   on the marry-go-round

check the

b Each ride on the merry-go-round costs 97 cents. If Ravi rides the merry-go-round 4 times, about how much does he have to pay?

97
× 4
38.8   he spends 38.8 cents

(continued on next page)

NAME _____ | DATE _____

Round & Round page 2 of 2

Show all your work when you solve these story problems.

3 Midge is a tiger shark and Bruce is a great white shark. Midge is 396 centimeters long and Bruce is 609 centimeters long. How many centimeters longer is Bruce than Midge?

$$\begin{array}{r} {}^{5}\;{}^{10}\\ -\,\,6\,0\,9\\ 3\,9\,6\\ \hline 2\,1\,3 \end{array}$$

Bruce is 213 centimeters long

4 Which equation does NOT describe the situation in problem 3?

○ $609 - 396 = c$ ● $396 + 609 = c$

○ $396 + c = 609$ ○ $609 - c = 396$

5 **CHALLENGE** The greater roadrunner (a bird that runs better than it flies) can run 16 miles per hour. A frightened ostrich can run 3 times faster.

a How fast can a frightened ostrich run?

$$\begin{array}{r} \times\,1\,6\\ 3\\ \hline 4\,8 \end{array}$$

the ostrich can run 48 miles per hour

b How far can a frightened ostrich run in half an hour?

$$\begin{array}{r} 2\,4\\ 2\,\overline{)4\,8}\\ 4\\ \overline{8}\\ 8 \end{array}$$

the ostrich can walk 24 miles in half an hour

c Fill in the boxes to complete an equation to represent problem 5b.

$16 \times \boxed{3} \div \boxed{48} = m$

48

🏠 Rounding to Tens & Hundreds page 1 of 2

Note to Families

This worksheet gives students practice rounding to the nearest ten and hundred. Round numbers to the nearest ten by checking the digit in the ones place. If that digit is 5 or greater, round up to the next ten. If the digit is 4 or less, the digit in the tens place stays the same. When you round to the nearest hundred, check the digit in the tens place. If that digit is 5 or greater, round up to the next hundred. If that digit is 4 or less, the digit in the hundreds place stays the same.

1 Round the following numbers to the nearest 10.

32	30	378	380	87	90
1,055	10 60 ✗		63	60	

2 Round the following numbers to the nearest 100.

213	200	347	400	59	100
408	400		2,665	?	91.9ʰ

3 Round the following:

	to the nearest 10	to the nearest 100
26	30	100 ✗
493	490	400 ✗
1,845	1,850 ✗	1,800
802	800	800
199	200 ✗	200 ✗

(continued on next page)

Rounding to Tens & Hundreds page 2 of 2

Show all your work for these problems.

4 Andy's class wants to help poor families in Guatemala grow their own food. A $35 donation to a relief organization will provide a family with the seeds and tools they need to build a vegetable garden.

35
4
2
140

a Mark the most reasonable estimate for how much it would cost to help 4 families build vegetable gardens:

○ $75.00 ◉ $100.00 ◉ $150.00 ○ $200.00

b What is the exact cost of seeds and tools for 4 family gardens through the relief organization?

the exact cost is 140 $ ✓

Help

c If Andy's class raises $167, how much money will be left over?

```
  167
- 140
   27
```

they have $27 left ✓

5 **CHALLENGE** A donation of $75 to the relief organization can bring a health counselor to a poor neighborhood in Indonesia to help mothers improve their children's health. Ms. Murray and Mr. Austin both have 30 students in their classes. If each child gives $5, how many neighborhoods can they provide health counselors for?

60
5
300

```
  30
×  5
 150
+150
```

```
    9
- 300 10
  75
 225
- 75
 150 10
  75
  75
- 75
  × ×
```

they can provide

3 neihborhoods

X

🏠 Two-Digit Addition, Card Collecting & Shopping page 1 of 2

1 Add each pair of numbers. Show all your work.

a 30 + 65 =	**b** 42 + 35 =	**c** 46 + 38 =
d 53 + 82	**e** 67 + 85	**f** 94 + 76

2 Henry had 126 baseball cards. His cousin gave him 20 more cards. Then Henry gave his brother 58 cards. How many baseball cards does Henry have now? Show all your work.

$$126 + 20 - 58$$

$$146 + 58$$

he has 88 cards now

(continued on next page)

Two-Digit Addition, Card Collecting & Shopping page 2 of 2

Show your work when you solve these problems.

3 DVD players are on sale for $84. That's $35 off the regular price. What is the regular price?

```
    8 4
+   3 5
  1 1 9
```

the regular price is 119 $

4 **CHALLENGE** MP3 players cost $85 each. Mark has a coupon that will take $15 off the total if he buys two. If he uses his coupon, how much will Mark pay for two MP3 players?

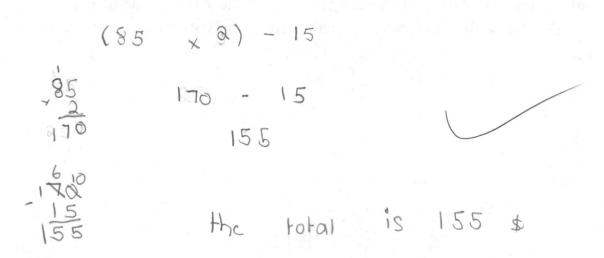

$(85 \times 2) - 15$

```
  85
×  2
 170
```

$170 - 15$

155

```
  170
-  15
  155
```

the total is 155 $

NAME _____ | **DATE** _____

🏠 Construction Paper, Scooters & Snails page 1 of 2

1 Solve the subtraction problems. Show all your work.

a 67 – 28 =	**b** 83 – 37 =
c 92 – 54 =	**d** 500 – 199 =

2 Mr. Jones needs 126 pieces of construction paper to do an art project with his students. He has a full pack with 50 sheets of paper and an open pack with some more sheets. How many more sheets of paper does he need to borrow from the teacher next door?

a Choose the information that will help you solve the problem.

○ There are 24 students in the class.

○ The open pack has 17 sheets of paper.

○ Packs of construction paper cost $3 each.

○ He has 32 pencils.

b Solve the problem. Show all your work. Write your answer on the line at the bottom of the page.

Mr. Jones needs to borrow _____ more sheets of paper.

(continued on next page)

Construction Paper, Scooters & Snails page 2 of 2

3 Angela wants to buy a scooter. She has saved $57 from birthday money and $19 more by doing gardening jobs for neighbors. The scooter costs $125. How much more money does Angela need?

a Estimate the amount of money Angela still needs, and explain your thinking. How did you get your estimate?

b Which equation does *not* represent this problem? (The letter *m* stands for money.)

○ $57 + $19 + m = $125

○ $125 – $57 – $19 = m

○ $125 + $57 + $19 = m

○ $125 – m = $57 + $19

c Figure out how much more money Angela actually needs to buy the scooter. Show your work.

4 **CHALLENGE** Lucy, a garden snail, laid 4 batches of eggs one summer. Each batch had 53 eggs, but 17 eggs from each batch didn't survive. How many of Lucy's eggs hatched into baby snails?

a Write an equation to represent this problem. Use the letter *s* to stand for baby snails.

b Solve the problem. Show all of your work.

NAME _____ | DATE _____

🏠 Estimates & Exact Answers page 1 of 2

1 Use estimation to answer each question yes or no.

a Sue has $346 dollars. She wants to buy a bike and still have $150 left. She found a bike that costs $189. Can she buy it and still have $150 left?

b Bruce decided to give away some of his 400 baseball cards. He wants to keep at least 150 of them. If Bruce gives one friend 167 cards and another friend 112 cards, will he have at least 150 left?

c Luis and Carlos are in a reading contest to see who can read the most pages. Luis wants to win by at least 150 pages. Carlos read 427 pages. If Luis reads 526 pages, will he win by at least 150 pages?

2 Estimate and solve.

○ First, estimate the difference between the two numbers.
You could round them and then subtract, or you could think about what you have to add to the smaller number to get to the bigger number.

○ Then find the exact difference between the two numbers.

○ Check your answer with your estimate to be sure it makes sense: if it doesn't make sense, check your work or do it another way.

Numbers to Subtract	Estimated Difference	Exact Difference
a 487 – 309		
b 1,825 – 643		

(continued on next page)

NAME _____ | DATE _____

Estimates & Exact Answers page 2 of 2

Show all your work when you solve these problems.

3 Angie's grandma lives in Cleveland, Ohio, and is going to drive to Minneapolis, Minnesota, to visit Angie and her family. The two cities are 752 travel miles apart, and it takes 12 hours to drive that far.

    a Angie's grandma wants to do the drive in two days. If she drives the same amount each day, how many miles will she drive each day?

    b How many hours will she spend driving each day?

4 **CHALLENGE** Christy's family is driving from St. Louis, Missouri, to Boston, Massachusetts, to visit her cousins. The distance is 1,162 miles, and the driving time is 17 hours and 38 minutes. Christy's mother wants to do the drive in 3 days, going about the same number of miles each day.

    a About how many miles will they drive each day?

    b About how many hours will they spend driving each day?

NAME _____ | **DATE** _____

 Jump Rope for Charity page 1 of 2

1 Solve each problem below. You may use any strategy that is efficient for you. Be sure to show your work.

a Tyson and Amanda are jumping rope to raise money for charity. Amanda jumped rope 295 times. Tyson jumped 316 times. How many times total did they jump?

b Beck and Sam are also jumping rope for charity. Beck jumped 345 times. Sam jumped 255 times. How many times did they jump in all?

c Loretta and Claire are shooting baskets to raise money for field trips. Loretta made 123 baskets. Claire made 128 baskets. How many baskets did they make together?

NAME _____ | DATE _____

Jump Rope for Charity page 2 of 2

2 Solve the two problems below, using any strategy you choose. Be sure to show your work.

275 + 336	189 + 332

3 **CHALLENGE** Stella and Colette are jumping rope to raise money for the local Children's Hospital. Every time they jump 100 times, they earn one dollar. Stella jumped 487 times. Collette jumped 464 times. Did Stella and Colette jump enough times to raise $10 for the Children's Hospital? Show all your work.

56

NAME _____ | DATE _____

 **Which Strategy?** page 1 of 2

Note to Families

At school, we have been exploring the standard (or traditional) algorithm for addition. Another name for this strategy is the regrouping method. We've compared the standard algorithm to other strategies we have learned this year. Ask your child questions about the strategies he or she is using.

1 Use the standard algorithm to solve each problem. Then solve it a different way. Label your method. Circle the strategy that seemed quicker and easier.

	Standard algorithm	Different
a 265 + 178 =		
b 213 + 198 =		
c 234 + 342		
d 168 + 143		

2 Conrad is making bread. After he mixes the ingredients together, he has to let the bread rise for 95 minutes. Then, the bread will bake for 58 minutes.

a How long will it take for the bread to rise and bake? Show your thinking using numbers, sketches, or words.

b What strategy did you use to solve this problem? Why?

(continued on next page)

NAME _____ | DATE _____

Which Strategy? page 2 of 2

3 Saima is training for a bike race. On Saturday, she rode her bike for 172 minutes. On Sunday, she rode for 153 minutes.

a How much longer did she ride her bike for on Saturday than on Sunday? Show your thinking using numbers, sketches, or words.

b What strategy did you use to solve this problem? Why?

c **CHALLENGE** Before she rides her bike, Saima warms up for 12 minutes. On Tuesday, Saima rode her bike for 52 miles. If it takes Saima 6 minutes to ride each mile, how long did it take for Saima to warm up and ride her bike on Tuesday?

Combinations of 1,000

4 Fill in the missing numbers to make a total of 1,000 in each box.

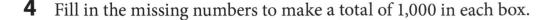

480 + [ ] = 1,000   670 + [ ] = 1,000   170 + [ ] = 1,000

210 + [ ] = 1,000   720 + [ ] = 1,000   500 + [ ] = 1,000

840 + [ ] = 1,000   360 + [ ] = 1,000

Estimates, Sums & Story Problems page 1 of 2

1 Round each pair of numbers to the nearest ten, and then add the rounded numbers to estimate the sum. Then use any strategy you like to find the exact sum. Compare the exact sum to your estimate to make sure that it makes sense. If your answer does not make sense, double-check your work or solve the problem another way.

Number to Add	Round & Add	Exact Sum	Check your answer if the sum and estimate were far apart.
a 386 + 275			
b 517 + 378			
c 263 + 477			

2 Use estimation to answer each question yes or no. Do not find exact sums.

a Shawna has a photo album with space for 160 pictures. She has 33 pictures of her family, 48 pictures from summer camp, and 57 pictures from school. Does she have enough pictures to fill the photo album?

b Fred needs 410 game markers to play a game with his classmates and their families on Family Math Night. He has 96 red markers, 123 blue markers, 106 yellow markers, and 72 green markers. Does he have enough game markers to play the game?

(continued on next page)

Estimates, Sums & Story Problems page 2 of 2

3 Jasmine's neighbor paid her $32 for helping with some yard work. Jasmine gave her brother $8 because he helped her with some of the work. Then she went shopping with the rest of the money. She bought 3 books that were $6 each and a bottle of juice for $2. How much money did she have left? Show all your work.

4 The third graders are putting on a play for the fourth and fifth graders. They need to set up chairs in the gym for the fourth and fifth graders to sit on. There are 86 fourth graders, 79 fifth graders, 3 fourth grade teachers, and 3 fifth grade teachers. How many chairs will the third graders need to set up? Show all your work.

5 **CHALLENGE** The third graders can put no more than 20 chairs in a row. How many rows of chairs will they need? Show all your work.

NAME _____ | **DATE** _____

🏠 Writing Time in Different Ways page 1 of 2

Word Bank				
1 one	2 two	3 three	4 four	5 five
6 six	7 seven	8 eight	9 nine	10 ten
11 eleven	12 twelve	20 twenty	30 thirty	40 forty
50 fifty	60 sixty	o'clock		

1 Write the time shown on each clock with numbers. Write it again with words.

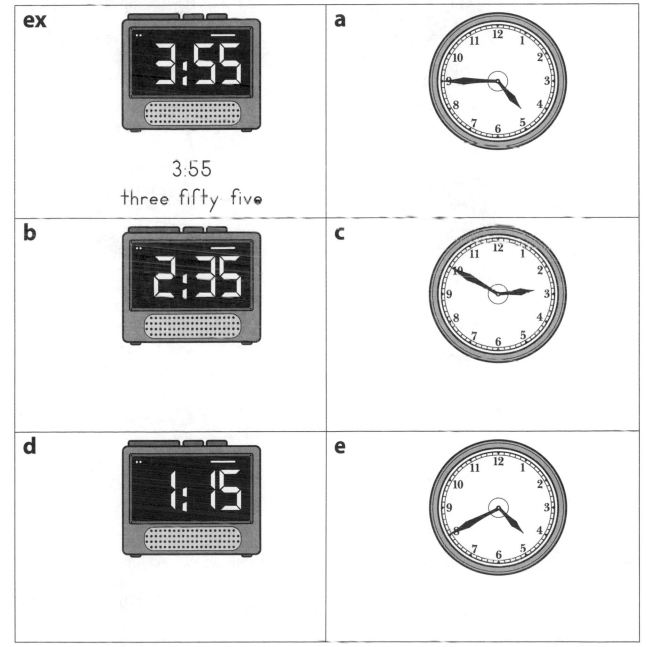

ex

3:55

three fifty five

a

b

c

d

e

2 How many minutes are there in an hour? _____ *(continued on next page)*

NAME | DATE

Writing Time in Different Ways page 2 of 2

Word Bank		
15 fifteen	30 thirty	45 forty-five
quarter past	half past	quarter 'til

3 Write the time shown on each clock with number words. Write it again with time telling words.

ex

four forty-five
quarter 'til five

a

b

c

d

e

4 **CHALLENGE** How many minutes are there in the following fractions of an hour?

$\frac{2}{4}$ of an hour _____ $\frac{3}{4}$ of an hour _____ $\frac{1}{3}$ of an hour _____

$\frac{1}{6}$ of an hour _____ $\frac{3}{6}$ of an hour _____ $\frac{1}{12}$ of an hour _____

$\frac{2}{3}$ of an hour _____ $\frac{5}{12}$ of an hour _____

 62

🏠 Annie's School Day page 1 of 2

1 Annie is a third grader at Bridger School. There are two clocks in her classroom. One is a digital clock, and the other is an analog clock with a regular clock face. Read the clocks below, and write the time to show when the class does different activities through the day.

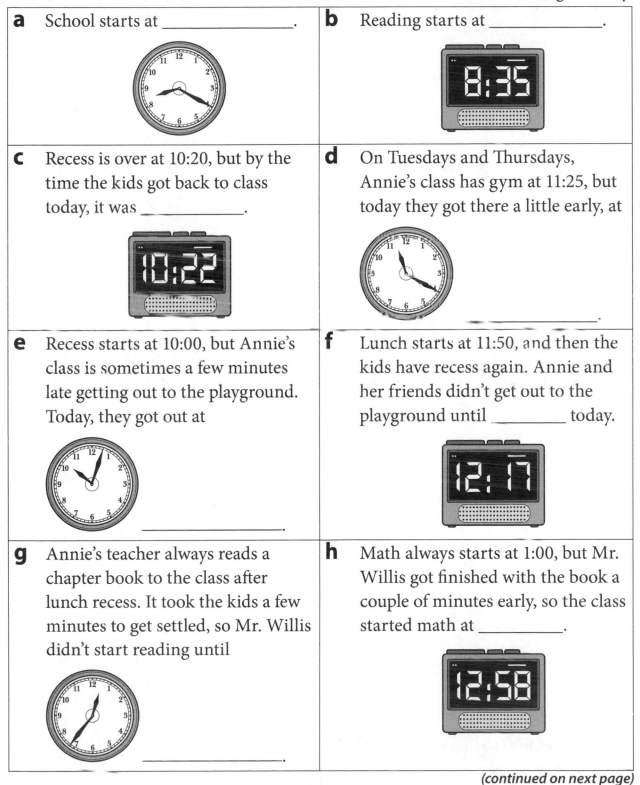

a School starts at _____.

b Reading starts at _____.

c Recess is over at 10:20, but by the time the kids got back to class today, it was _____.

d On Tuesdays and Thursdays, Annie's class has gym at 11:25, but today they got there a little early, at _____.

e Recess starts at 10:00, but Annie's class is sometimes a few minutes late getting out to the playground. Today, they got out at _____.

f Lunch starts at 11:50, and then the kids have recess again. Annie and her friends didn't get out to the playground until _____ today.

g Annie's teacher always reads a chapter book to the class after lunch recess. It took the kids a few minutes to get settled, so Mr. Willis didn't start reading until _____.

h Math always starts at 1:00, but Mr. Willis got finished with the book a couple of minutes early, so the class started math at _____.

(continued on next page)

NAME _____ | DATE _____

Annie's School Day page 2 of 2

Show your thinking in numbers, words, or sketches when you solve these problems.

2 Annie measured the cover of her library book using jumbo paperclips. She found that it is 5 paperclips high and $4\frac{1}{2}$ paperclips wide. A jumbo paperclip is 5 centimeters long.

a How many centimeters high is the cover of Annie's library book?

b How many centimeters wide is the cover of Annie's book?

3 **CHALLENGE** Annie's reading class begins at 8:35 and lasts 1 hour and 45 minutes. What time is her reading class over? Show two different ways to find the answer.

a One way:

b Another way:

Annie's reading class is over at _____.

🏠 Measuring Mass & Weight page 1 of 2

1 Read the scale. How much does the kitten weigh?

2 Look at the pan balance scale. What is the mass of the turtle?

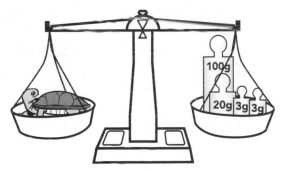

3 The _____ of the box of

crayons is _____.

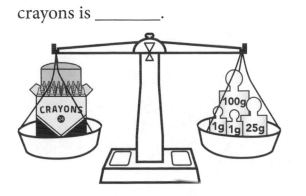

4 Read the scale. How much do the oranges weigh?

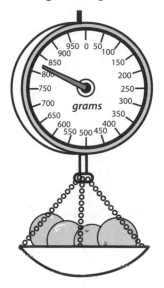

5 Look at the pan balance scale. What is the mass of the bag of potatoes in grams? Show your work.

(continued on next page)

NAME | DATE

Measuring Mass & Weight page 2 of 2

6 What is the total mass of Sarina's lunch, including her lunchbox, if her sandwich is 180 grams, her apple is 125 grams, and her cookies are 35 grams each? The lunch box itself has a mass of 350 grams. Sarina has 4 cookies in her lunch. Show your work.

7 Draw the hands on the analog clocks to show the times on the digital clocks for **a** and **b** below. Write the times shown on the analog clocks on the digital clocks for **c** and **d** below.

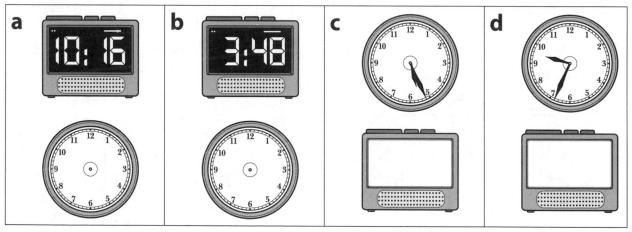

8 **CHALLENGE:** Sarina's piano teacher gave her a large candy bar. One serving weighs 39 grams. The candy bar has 2 and a half servings. How many grams does the whole candy bar weigh? Show all of your thinking.

NAME _____ | DATE _____

🏠 Metric Measures of Mass & Liquid Volume page 1 of 2

1 What unit would you use to measure the mass of the following items? Circle the correct answer.

a The mass of an envelope

    grams   kilograms

b The amount of soda a straw can hold

    milliliters   liters

c The mass of a 3rd grader.

    grams   kilograms

d The amount of milk in a container at school

    milliliters   liters

e The mass of a loaf of bread

    grams   kilograms

f The amount of water used to take a bath

    milliliters   liters

g The amount of milk in a cake recipe

    milliliters   liters

h The amount of gasoline in a car

    milliliters   liters

i The mass of an apple

    grams   kilograms

j The amount of cough medicine you take

    milliliters   liters

k The mass of a television

    grams   kilograms

(continued on next page)

NAME _____ | DATE _____

Metric Measures of Mass & Liquid Volume page 2 of 2

2 Go on a scavenger hunt at home. Try to find objects that have a mass of about 1 gram and about 1 kilogram. Record them below.

1 gram (g)	1 kilogram (kg)

3 Now try to find containers that hold about 1 milliliter and 1 liter. Record them below.

1 milliliter (ml)	1 liter (l)

4 What object in your home do you think has the most mass?

a About how much mass does it have in kilograms?

b What object in your home probably has the least mass?

5 What container in your home do you think has the largest capacity (holds the most liquid)?

a About how many liters do you think it holds?

b What container in your home probably has the smallest capacity?

NAME _____ **| DATE** _____

 Grasshopper Math page 1 of 2

Grasshoppers are insects that can jump 10 times their height. Help Greg Grasshopper solve the problems below. Use the correct unit in your answer. Use numbers, sketches, or words to show your work.

1 Greg Grasshopper has a mass of 3 grams. He climbs onto a leaf with 9 other grasshoppers that each have a mass of 3 grams. Then 4 grasshoppers jump off of the leaf. What is the total mass of the grasshoppers that are still on the leaf?

2 Greg Grasshopper lives in a rectangular garden. One side of the garden is 134 cm long. The other side is 277 cm long. If Greg Grasshopper walks all the way around his garden 2 times, how far has he walked?

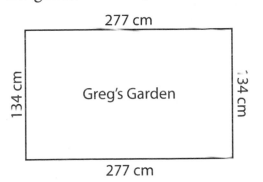

277 cm

134 cm   Greg's Garden   134 cm

277 cm

3 Walking always makes Greg Grasshopper hungry. After he walked around his garden twice, he ate 387 milligrams of grass and 246 milligrams of leaves. How many milligrams did he eat?

4 Then Greg was tired. He fell asleep for 2 hours. When he woke up, it was 3:45. What time did he fall asleep?

(continued on next page)

NAME _____ | DATE _____

Grasshopper Math page 2 of 2

5 Greg Grasshopper has three cousins: Gary, Grant, and Garth. They all can jump 10 times farther than their length. Figure out how many jumps each cousin needs to make to travel a distance of 9 meters. (Hint: There are 100 centimeters in a meter.) Use numbers, sketches, or words to show your work.

a Gary is 3 centimeters long.

Gary has to make _____ jumps to travel a distance of 9 meters.

b Garth is 5 centimeters long.

Garth has to make _____ jumps to travel a distance of 9 meters.

c **CHALLENGE** Grant is 4 centimeters long.

Grant has to make _____ jumps to travel a distance of 9 meters.

  70

🏠 Sharing Candy Bars & Measuring page 1 of 2

1 You are sharing a candy bar with friends.

a If you share with one person, there are two of you sharing. How do you write your share?

b If you share with two people, there are three of you sharing. How do you write your share?

c Would you have more candy if you share with one person or two people? Explain your answer.

2 Circle the appropriate words to fill in the blanks.

a A bowling ball is heavy! I would measure its _____ with _____.

mass	length	volume

liters	kilograms	grams

b A sun jellyfish is pretty long. I would measure its _____ with _____.

mass	length	volume

liters	kilograms	centimeters

c A water bottle doesn't hold much. I would measure its _____ with _____.

mass	length	volume

liters	kilograms	milliliters

d A giraffe is tall. I would measure its _____ with _____.

mass	height	volume

liters	kilograms	meters

e An elephant eats lots! I would measure the _____ of its food with _____.

mass	length	volume

liters	kilograms	meters

f An Etruscan shrew is short. I would measure its _____ with _____.

mass	length	volume

liters	kilograms	centimeters

g An Etruscan shrew is light. I would measure its _____ with _____.

mass	length	volume

grams	kilograms	meters

h That bucket holds a lot! I would measure its _____ with _____.

mass	length	volume

liters	kilograms	meters

(continued on next page)

Sharing Candy Bars & Measuring page 2 of 2

Show all your thinking with numbers, words, or sketches for each of the problems below. Label your answers with the correct units.

3 A bottle of Charlie's favorite brand of orange juice has 7 servings. Each serving is 240 milliliters (ml).

a How many milliliters of orange juice are in the whole bottle?

b Is that more or less than 2 liters? (Hint: 1 liter = 1,000 milliliters)

4 **CHALLENGE** A box of soup contains 4 servings. Each serving has $4\frac{1}{2}$ grams of fat and 720 milligrams of sodium.

a If someone was really hungry and ate all 4 servings in the box, how many grams of fat would that person eat?

b How many milligrams (mg) of sodium would that person eat? (1 gram = 1,000 milligrams)

c It is recommended that people eat no more than 2,400 mg of sodium in a day. If a person ate a whole box of the soup, would that person take in more or less than 2,400 mg?

d How many milligrams more or less?

NAME _____ | DATE _____

Measurement & Fractions page 1 of 2

1 Circle the appropriate words to fill in the blank.

a A piece of paper is light! I would measure its _____ with _____.

mass	length	volume		milliliters	grams	centimeters

b That pencil is short! I would measure its _____ with _____.

mass	length	volume		milliliters	grams	centimeters

c A soda can doesn't hold very much. I would measure its _____ with _____.

mass	length	volume		milliliters	grams	centimeters

2 Circle your answer.

a Which is longer—half of a day or half of an hour?

b Which is heavier—half of a gram or half of a kilogram?

c Which holds more—half of a milliliter or half of a liter?

3 Write the correct symbol: < or > or =

$\dfrac{1}{4}$ ▢ $\dfrac{1}{10}$ $\dfrac{1}{4}$ ▢ $\dfrac{1}{2}$ $\dfrac{1}{4}$ ▢ 1

4 Choose one pair of fractions from problem 3. Discuss your answer. How do you know that one of the numbers is more than the other?

5 Divide the shape into the number of parts you need, and shade in the fraction $\frac{1}{3}$.

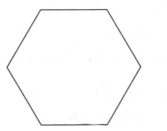

(continued on next page)

NAME _____ | DATE _____

Measurement & Fractions page 2 of 2

6 My friends and I are sharing a candy bar. I got $\frac{1}{4}$ of the candy bar, and my friend Abby got $\frac{1}{4}$ of it. How much is left? Explain your answer.

7 Tam filled his wading pool with 150 liters of water. Then 138 liters splashed out. How many liters are still in the pool? Write and solve an equation to represent the problem.

8 A bottle of Lilly's favorite soda contains 590 milliliters of soda, has 260 calories, and 70 grams of carbohydrates. Lilly is going to share the bottle with Maddy, so each will get half the bottle. Show your work. Include the unit of measurement in your answer.

a How many milliliters of soda will Lilly drink?

b How many calories will Maddy get?

c How many grams of carbohydrates will each girl get?

Use a separate sheet of paper to show your thinking using words, sketches, or numbers to solve the problems below.

9 **CHALLENGE** Chris is looking at a map to see how many miles it is from Golden Valley, where he lives, to Willow Lake, where his grandmother lives. The map uses a scale where $1\frac{1}{2}$ inches represents 12 miles.

a Chris measured the map distance between the two towns and found that it is 6 inches. How many miles is it from Golden Valley to Willow Lake?

b Chris will take the train to Willow Lake. The train goes 60 miles an hour. If Chris takes the 2:20 train, about what time will he get to Willow Lake?

🏠 Fractions, Fractions & Fractions page 1 of 2

1 Complete the missing information below by writing in the fraction number or sketching the given fraction on a number line.

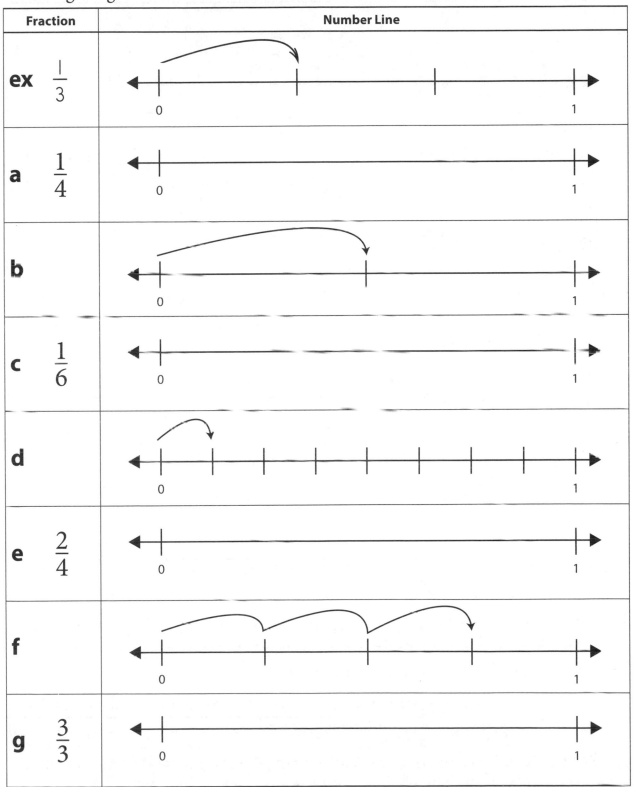

Fraction	Number Line
ex $\frac{1}{3}$	
a $\frac{1}{4}$	
b	
c $\frac{1}{6}$	
d	
e $\frac{2}{4}$	
f	
g $\frac{3}{3}$	

(continued on next page)

Fractions, Fractions & Fractions page 2 of 2

2 Use a < (less than), > (greater than) or = (equal) symbol to compare the following fraction pairs. Show your thinking by placing the fractions on the number line.

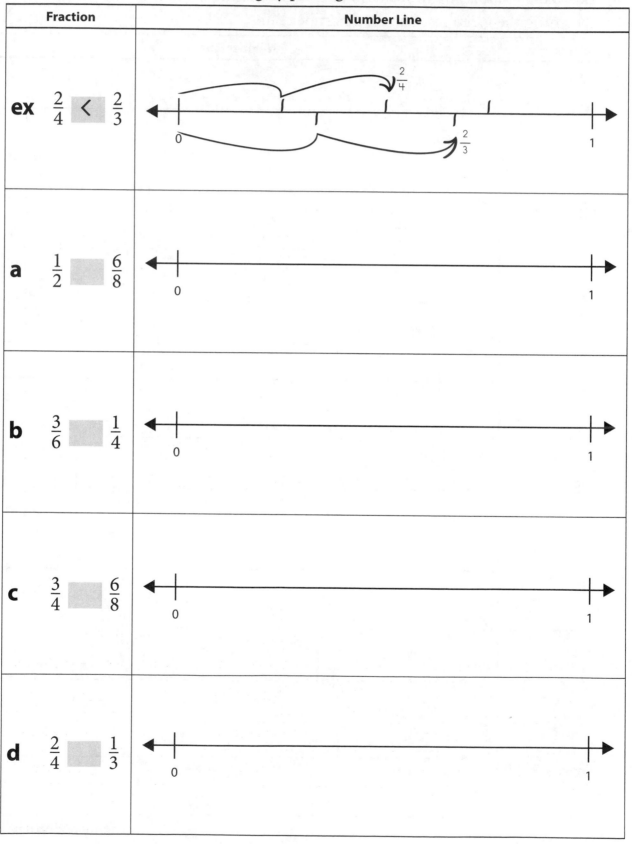

Fraction	Number Line
ex $\frac{2}{4}$ < $\frac{2}{3}$	
a $\frac{1}{2}$ ☐ $\frac{6}{8}$	
b $\frac{3}{6}$ ☐ $\frac{1}{4}$	
c $\frac{3}{4}$ ☐ $\frac{6}{8}$	
d $\frac{2}{4}$ ☐ $\frac{1}{3}$	

🏠 Snack Time: Mass, Volume & Length page 1 of 2

1 Use numbers, words, or sketches to show your thinking for problems a, b, and c. Don't forget to include the unit of measurement in your answers.

a Carl ate an apple that had a mass of 184 grams. Then, he ate 196 grams of peanuts. What was the total mass of Carl's snack?

b Allegra drank 203 milliliters of water. Then, she drank 157 milliliters of lemonade. How many milliliters of liquid did Allegra drink in all?

c Mr. Alcott's class was eating licorice twists for a special treat. They ate 117 feet of licorice twists. Mrs. Austen's class was also eating licorice twists. They ate 79 feet of licorice twists. How many more feet of licorice twists did Mr. Alcott's class eat?

2 What unit do you use? Circle the unit you would use for each type of measurement.

Length	liters	kilograms	centimeters
Mass	grams	inches	milliliters
Volume	milligrams	milliliters	meters

(continued on next page)

Snack Time: Mass, Volume & Length page 2 of 2

Use numbers, words, or sketches to show your thinking for all these problems. Don't forget to include the unit of measurement in your answers.

3 Mike has a can of potato chips. There are 16 chips in one serving, and one serving weighs 28 grams.

a How many grams do 3 servings weigh?

b One serving of the potato chips has 150 calories. How many calories are in 3 servings?

c One serving of the potato chips has 160 milligrams of sodium. How many milligrams of sodium are in 3 servings?

4 One can of potato chips has 5 servings. Each serving has 15 grams of carbohydrates.

a How many grams of carbohydrates are in a whole can of potato chips?

b **CHALLENGE** How many cans of potato chips are needed for 14 people to each have 3 servings?

🏠 Time & Fraction Review page 1 of 2

1 Fill in the circle next to the time shown on each clock.

a ○ 1:45
○ 1:47
○ 2:47
○ 9:09

b ○ 3:40
○ 8:04
○ 8:19
○ 8:20

2 Write the time shown on each clock.

a _____ : _____

b _____ : _____

3 Circle the digital clock that shows the same time as this analog clock.

4 Taylor's mom said he and his brother could go to a movie while she went shopping. She dropped them off at the theater at 1:45 and said she would be back at 4:00 to get them. They had three choices of movies. Which movie could they see and be done by the time their mom came to get them? Show all your work. Hint: Remember that there are 60 minutes in an hour.

Movie	Start Time	Length (Including Previews)
Beetle goes to Town	1:55	130 minutes
Arctic Adventure	2:00	125 minutes
Rainy Day Dog	2:15	100 minutes

(continued on next page)

Time & Fraction Review page 2 of 2

5 On each square, fill in a fraction of the square that is less than $\frac{1}{2}$. Then use the symbols >, =, or < to compare your fraction to $\frac{1}{2}$.

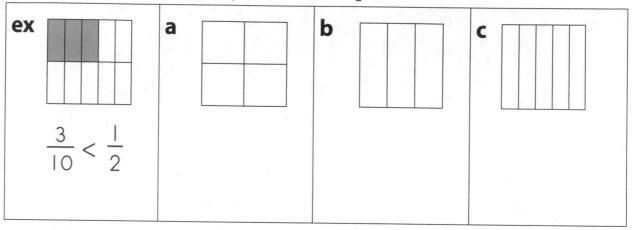

ex $\frac{3}{10} < \frac{1}{2}$ a   b   c

6 On each square, fill in a fraction of the square that is greater than $\frac{1}{2}$. Then use the symbols >, =, or < to compare your fraction to $\frac{1}{2}$.

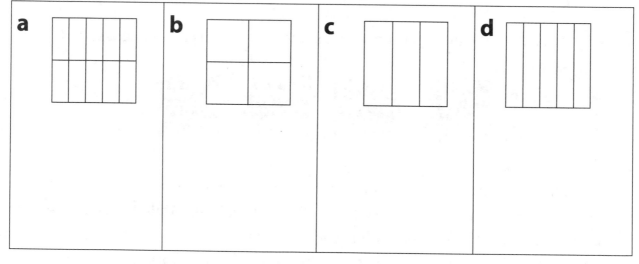

a   b   c   d

7 Write each of the following fractions where they belong on the number line below.

$$\frac{9}{10} \qquad \frac{1}{4} \qquad \frac{2}{5} \qquad \frac{2}{3}$$

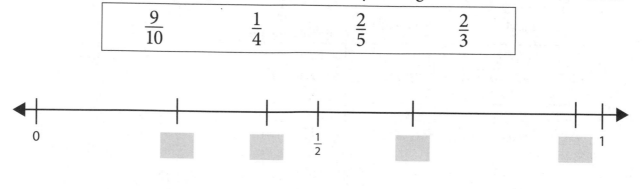

 **Sharing Money** page 1 of 2

Show your work as you solve these problems.

1 Tom and Zara have a dog-walking business. They walk their customers' dogs together and share all the money they make equally.

a On Monday they made $4.00. How much does each of them get?

b On Tuesday they made $5.00. How much does Tom get?

c On Wednesday they made $5.50. How much does Zara get?

2 Lately, Tom and Zara and their little sister, Molly, have been incredibly lucky at finding money.

a On the way home from school on Thursday they found $3.00. How much does each one get if the three of them share equally?

b On Friday they found $6.00. How much does each one get?

3 a Tom, Zara, Molly, and their cousin, Kerry, are sharing $4.00. How much does Tom get?

b Now the four of them are sharing $8.00. How much does Zara get?

c If Tom, Zara, Molly, and Kerry share $2.00, how much does Molly get?

d If the four of them share $1.00, how much does Kerry get?

(continued on next page)

Sharing Money page 2 of 2

Show your work when you solve these problems.

4 Erin and Devon are playing a game. Erin has 42 points. If Devon had 14 more points, he'd have double the points Erin has. How many points does Devon have?

5 **CHALLENGE** The kids in Mrs. B's class did a survey about their favorite flavors of ice cream. One-fourth of the class likes strawberry the best. One-half of the class likes chocolate the best. The rest of the class, 7 kids, said vanilla is their favorite ice cream flavor. How many kids are in Mrs. B's class?

NAME _____ | **DATE** _____

🏠 Multiply & Divide by 4 & 8

1 Fill in the missing numbers. Also write an equation for each picture.

ex 1 skateboard has __4__ wheels. __$1 \times 4 = 4$__

ex 2 skateboards have __8__ wheels. __$2 \times 4 = 8$__

a 3 skateboards have _____ wheels. _____

b 4 skateboards have _____ wheels. _____

c 5 skateboards have _____ wheels. _____

d 10 skateboards have _____ wheels. _____

2 My friends and I went to the skateboard park. We saw 16 wheels rolling up and down the ramps. How many skateboards did we see? Fill in the bubble beside the matching expression and fill in the answer.

○ $15 \div 3 =$ _____   ○ $16 \div 2 =$ _____

○ $16 \div 4 =$ _____   ○ $24 \div 6 =$ _____

(continued on next page)

83

NAME _____ | DATE _____

Multiply & Divide by 4 & 8

3 Fill in the missing numbers. Also write an equation for each picture.

ex 1 octopus has __8__ legs. __1 × 8 = 8__

ex 2 octopuses have __16__ legs. __2 × 8 = 16__

a 3 octopuses have _____ legs. _____

b 4 octopuses have _____ legs. _____

c 5 octopuses have _____ legs. _____

d 10 octopuses have _____ legs. _____

4 James and his brother went to the Sea Life Aquarium. When they got to the octopus tank, they saw 24 legs waving at them. How many optopuses did they see in the tank? Fill in the bubble beside the matching expression and fill in the answer.

○ 24 ÷ 6 = _____

○ 24 ÷ 8 = _____

○ 8 ÷ 8 = _____

○ 24 × 2 = _____

NAME _____ | DATE _____

🏠 Telling Time to the Minute page 1 of 2

1 Fill in the circle next to the time shown on each clock.

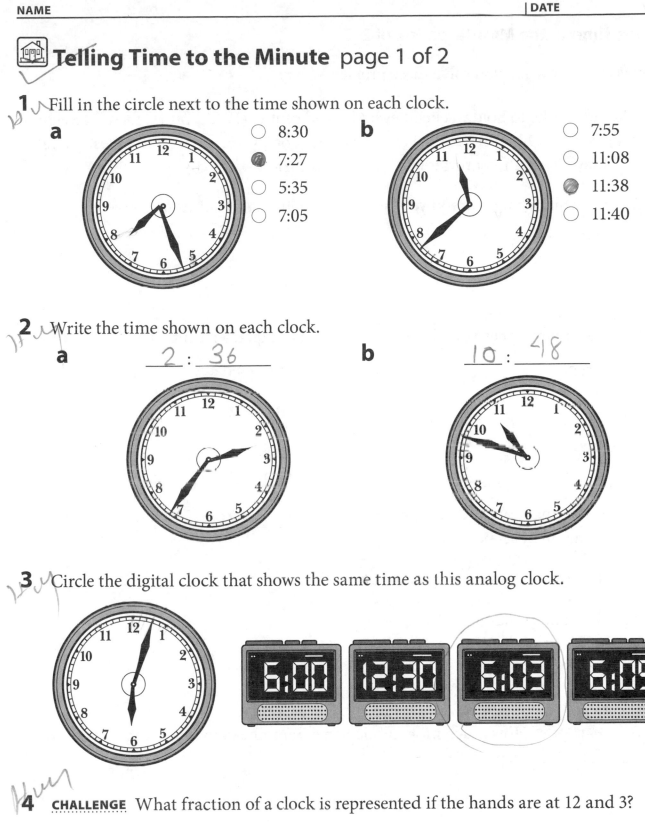

a
- ○ 8:30
- ● 7:27
- ○ 5:35
- ○ 7:05

b
- ○ 7:55
- ○ 11:08
- ● 11:38
- ○ 11:40

2 Write the time shown on each clock.

a   2 : 36

b   10 : 48

3 Circle the digital clock that shows the same time as this analog clock.

4 **CHALLENGE** What fraction of a clock is represented if the hands are at 12 and 3?

(continued on next page)

NAME _____ | DATE _____

Telling Time to the Minute page 2 of 2

Show your work when you solve these problems.

5 Bike riders like to hold weekend events called centuries. A century, for a bike rider, is a ride that's 100 miles long. For people who don't want to ride 100 miles in one day, they have half-centuries and quarter-centuries.

a How many miles would you ride if you rode a half-century?

50 miles ✓

b How many miles would you ride if you rode a quarter-century?

25 miles ✓

6 Sarah is saving money to buy a microscope. She has saved $25 so far. That's $\frac{1}{3}$ of the cost of the microscope.

a How much does the microscope cost?

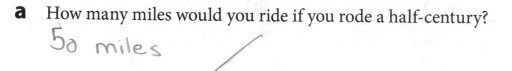

25 | 25 | 25 $\frac{25}{3} = 75$ 75 $ in all ✓

b **CHALLENGE** How much more money does Sarah need to save to have $\frac{1}{2}$ the cost of the microscope?

50 $ maybe

37.5 − 25 ✓

= 12.5

NAME _____ | DATE _____

🏠 Multiplication & Division Review page 1 of 2

1 Complete the multiplication facts.

2	4	7	2	10	9	7
× 3	× 5	× 5	× 6	× 8	× 2	× 3
6	20	35	12	80	18	21

0	5	7	3	9	5	3
× 2	× 6	× 2	× 5	× 5	× 5	× 8
0	30	14	15	45	25	24

8	5	7	4	6	7	4
× 2	× 8	× 1	× 6	× 6	× 4	× 8
16	40	7	24	36	28	32

2 Complete the division facts.

$10 \div 5 =$ ___2___ $9 \div 1 =$ ___9___ $20 \div 10 =$ ___2___

$50 \div 5 =$ ___10___ $30 \div 5 =$ ___6___ $18 \div 2 =$ ___9___

3 Frank, Joe, and Carl went with their grandma to the bakery. She said that they could use the change she got back to buy mini-chip cookies to share equally. She bought a cake for $11 and two loaves of bread for $2.70 each. She paid with a $20 bill. The mini-chip cookies cost 40¢ each. How many cookies did each boy get? Show all your work.

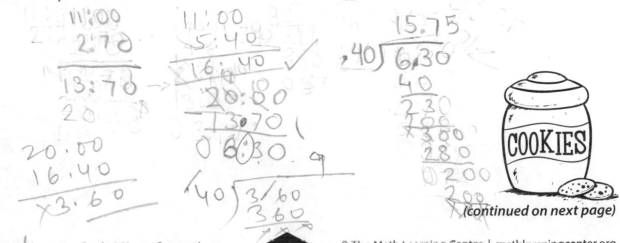

(continued on next page)

Multiplication & Division Review page 2 of 2

4 **a** Rosa and Clarice are making sandwiches for all the students in their class and their teacher. There are 23 students in their class. Each loaf of bread has 16 slices. They don't want to use the slices on the ends of the bread, because most students don't like them. If they make 1 sandwich for each student and for the teacher, how many loaves of bread will they need? Show all your work.

they will need 2 lofs and
5 piccs left

b Rosa and Clarice realized they would have some bread left over (not including the end pieces), so they decided to make sandwiches for the librarian, office staff, and custodian. How many sandwiches will they be able to make?

5 sandwhichs

🏠 Multiplying by 2, 3, 4 & 8 page 1 of 2

1 Circle all the Doubles facts (×2) in blue. Then go back and do them.

2 Circle all the Doubles Plus One Set facts (×3) in red. Then go back and do them.

4 ×2 **8**	3 ×3 **9**	2 ×3 **6**	6 ×2 **12**	2 ×6 **12**
5 ×2 **10**	3 ×10 **30**	8 ×3 **24**	0 ×2 **0**	1 ×3 **3**
5 ×3 **15**	2 ×1 **2**	8 ×2 **16**	3 ×9 **27**	2 ×2 **4**
6 ×3 **18**	10 ×2 **20**	3 ×7 **21**	4 ×3 **12**	7 ×2 **14**

3 Now solve the division problems below. Use the multiplication facts above to help.

$9 \div 3 = \underline{3}$ $16 \div 8 = \underline{2}$ $21 \div 7 = \underline{3}$ $14 \div 7 = \underline{2}$ $10 \div 5 = \underline{2}$

$12 \div 4 = \underline{3}$ $20 \div 10 = \underline{2}$ $15 \div 5 = \underline{3}$ $24 \div 8 = \underline{3}$ $6 \div 3 = \underline{2}$

(continued on next page)

Multiplying by 2, 3, 4 & 8 page 2 of 2

4 Circle all the Double-Doubles facts (×4) in blue. Then go back and do them.

5 Circle all the Double-Double-Doubles facts (×8) in red. Then go back and do them.

8 × 3 24	4 × 9 36	10 × 4 40	5 × 8 40	2 × 4 8
0 × 4 0	8 × 1 8	7 × 8 56	3 × 4 12	10 × 8 80
4 × 5 20	6 × 4 24	8 × 8 64	7 × 4 28	6 × 8 48
9 × 8 72	8 × 4 32	4 × 4 16	8 × 3 24	2 × 8 16

6 Now solve the division problems below. Use the multiplication facts above to help.

$24 \div 3 = \underline{8}$ $16 \div 4 = \underline{4}$ $32 \div 4 = \underline{8}$ $56 \div 7 = \underline{8}$ $24 \div 6 = \underline{4}$

$48 \div 6 = \underline{}$ $40 \div 10 = \underline{4}$ $28 \div 7 = \underline{4}$ $16 \div 2 = \underline{8}$ $40 \div 5 = \underline{4}$

7 **CHALLENGE** Use what you know about the basic multiplication and division facts to solve the combinations below.

4 × 20 80	3 × 30 90	5 × 50 250	6 × 70 420	8 × 80 640

$80 \div 2 = \underline{40}$ $60 \div 3 = \underline{20}$ $90 \div 3 = \underline{30}$ $120 \div 4 \underline{30}$ $150 \div 5 = \underline{30}$

🏠 More Number Puzzles page 1 of 2

1 Draw a line from each expression on the left to the equivalent expression on the right.

ex	3×5		5×1
a	6×10		2×8
b	$20 \div 4$		$30 \div 2$
c	16×1		2×4
d	$24 \div 3$		15×2
e	6×4		8×3
f	6×5		2×30

2 Write an equal (=), greater than (>), or less than (<) sign in the boxes to make each equation true.

ex 2×5 ⟨ 3×4

a $12 \div 4$ ☐ 3×1 **b** 5×1 ☐ $12 \div 3$ **c** 8×2 ☐ 4×4

d $25 \div 5$ ☐ 4×2 **e** 8×4 ☐ 12×2 **f** $20 \div 2$ ☐ 3×5

3 Dani says you can show the solution to $2 \times 5 \times 3$ with one equation:
$2 \times 5 = 10 \times 3 = 30$

Maya says you have to use two equations:
$2 \times 5 = 10$ *and* $10 \times 3 = 30$

a Which student is correct? _____

b Explain your answer.

(continued on next page)

More Number Puzzles page 2 of 2

4 Andy had 30 marbles. He gave half of his marbles to his 3 cousins. His 3 cousins divided the marbles equally.

Jan had 48 marbles. She gave half of her marbles to her 4 cousins. Her 4 cousins divided the marbles equally.

a Whose cousins got more marbles, Andy's cousins or Jan's cousins? _____

b Use labeled sketches, numbers, or words to prove your answer.

5 Tim went to the pet store. He saw 3 cages of mice. There were 4 mice in each cage. He also saw 2 cages of hamsters. There were 6 hamsters in each cage. How many animals did Tim see in all?

a Circle the expression that best represents this problem.

$(3 \times 2) + (6 \times 4) = a$ $(3 \times 4) + (2 \times 6) = a$ $(4 \times 1) + (2 \times 3) = a$

b Then find the answer. Show your work.

6 **CHALLENGE** Use the digits 0–9 each just one time. Write them in the boxes below. Make each multiplication problem correct.

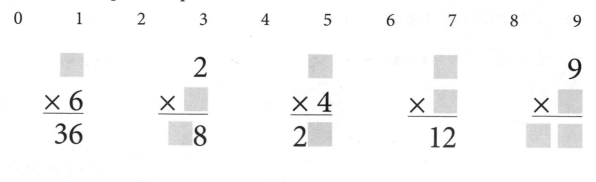

More Division Practice page 1 of 2

1 Fill in the blanks.

a $4 \times \underline{6} = 24$ $24 \div 4 = \underline{6}$

b $36 \div 9 = \underline{4}$ $9 \times \underline{4} = 36$

c $\underline{7} \times 5 = 35$ $35 \div \underline{7} = 5$

d $21 \div \underline{3} = 7$ $\underline{3} \times 7 = 21$

e $4 \times 3 = \underline{12}$ $\underline{12} \div 4 = 3$

f $\underline{6 \times 9} = 9 \times 6$ $\underline{54} \div 9 = 6$

g $403 + 296 = \underline{699}$

h $403 - 296 = \underline{7}$

2 Solve the story problems below. Show your thinking in words, numbers, or sketches for each one. Be sure to label your answers with the correct units.

a   Mr. Bee bought 3 jars of honey, which weighed a total of 24 ounces. If all the jars weighed the same amount, how much did each jar weigh?

$$3 \overline{)\,24} \quad 8$$

Each jar weighed __8 ounces__.

b   Mrs. Bee also bought 24 ounces of honey. She put 3 ounces of honey into several small jars. How many jars did she use?

$$3 \overline{)\,24} \quad 8$$

Mrs. Bee used __8 jars__.

3 Compare problems 2a and 2b. How are they alike? How are they different?

Promble 2a and 2b have the same answer but promble a is talking about onces and promble b is taking about Jars

(continued on next page)

NAME _____ | DATE _____

More Division Practice page 2 of 2

4 Mrs. Moth picked 8 flowers. Each flower had 6 petals.

a How many petals are on the flowers that Mrs. Moth picked? Show your work.

= 48 petels

b Write an equation that describes problem 4a. ___6 × 8 = 48___

5 CHALLENGE Later, Mrs. Moth picked 24 more flowers. Six of them each had 9 petals, 7 of them each had 8 petals, 5 of them each had 3 petals, and the rest each had 10 petals.

a How many flowers had 10 petals? Show your work.

(6 + 7 + 5) × ... (5 × 3)

5 18 ...

6 flower have 10 petels

b How many petals were on all 24 of the flowers that Mrs. Moth picked? Show your work.

· (9 × 6) + (7 × 8) + (5 × 3) + (6 × 10)

54   +   56   +   15   +   60

110   +   75

185

Division & Fraction Review page 1 of 2

1 Complete the division facts. They may help you with the next problem.

$20 \div 4 =$ __5__ $18 \div 3 =$ __6__ $15 \div 3 =$ __5__

$16 \div 4 =$ __4__ $16 \div 2 =$ __8__ $20 \div 5 =$ __4__

2 Divide each set into equal groups. Shade in some circles as directed.

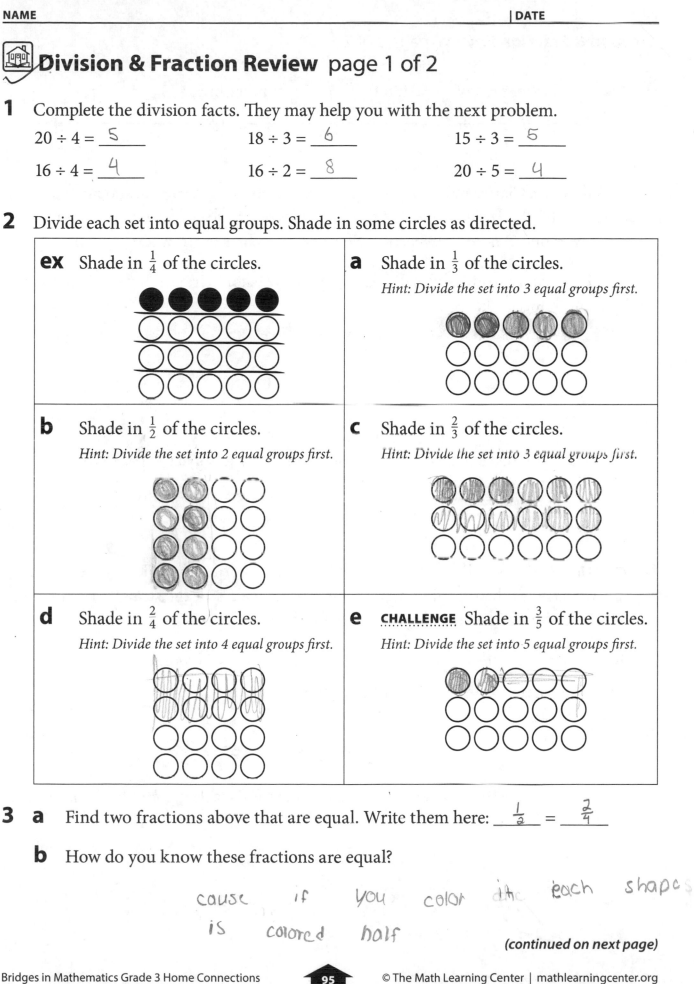

ex Shade in $\frac{1}{4}$ of the circles.

a Shade in $\frac{1}{3}$ of the circles.
Hint: Divide the set into 3 equal groups first.

b Shade in $\frac{1}{2}$ of the circles.
Hint: Divide the set into 2 equal groups first.

c Shade in $\frac{2}{3}$ of the circles.
Hint: Divide the set into 3 equal groups first.

d Shade in $\frac{2}{4}$ of the circles.
Hint: Divide the set into 4 equal groups first.

e **CHALLENGE** Shade in $\frac{3}{5}$ of the circles.
Hint: Divide the set into 5 equal groups first.

3 a Find two fractions above that are equal. Write them here: __$\frac{1}{2}$__ = __$\frac{2}{4}$__

b How do you know these fractions are equal?

cause   if   you   color   the   each   shapes
is   colored   half

(continued on next page)

NAME _____ | **DATE** _____

Division & Fraction Review page 2 of 2

4 Mark and label each of these fractions on the number line: $\frac{1}{2}$, $1\frac{1}{4}$, $1\frac{1}{3}$, $1\frac{3}{4}$.

5 David, Mary, Claire, and Mark were picking strawberries in their grandparents' garden. They had each picked the same number of strawberries when their grandma gave everyone 2 more strawberries. Now the 4 kids had 36 strawberries in all.

a How many strawberries did each child have before Grandma gave them more? Show your work.

$4 \div 36$

each kid had 9

b Mark the *two* equations below that could help you solve the problem.

○ $(s + 2) \times 4 = 36$ ○ $2 \times 4 + s = 36$

○ $36 - (2 \times 4) = s$ ● $(36 \div 4) - 2 = s$

6 **CHALLENGE** The next day the kids picked 124 strawberries in all. They gave $\frac{1}{4}$ of the strawberries to their neighbor, and their mother used $\frac{2}{4}$ of the strawberries in a pie. The rest of the strawberries were saved for snacks.

a How many strawberries went into the pie? Show your work.

$\frac{31}{124} \times \frac{1}{4}$ $\frac{124}{1} \times \frac{4}{1} = \frac{486 = 243}{31}$

b How many strawberries did the family have for snacking on? Show your work.

$\frac{31}{\frac{2}{62}}$ $\frac{31}{124} \times \frac{2}{4} = \frac{62}{31}$

NAME _____ | DATE _____

Unit 5 Review page 2 of 2

5 Solve each of the story problems belo
room. Use numbers, labeled sketches
equation to represent the problem an

a The pet store just got 32 new turt
She puts 4 turtles in each terrariu

$32 \div 4 = 8$

My equation: ___$32 \div 4 =$___

ngle. Write two (or more) different
the area.

Equations:

$3 + 3 + 3 + 3 = 12$

$4 + 4 + 4 = 12$

$3 \times 4 = 12$

$(3 \times 2) + (3 \times 2) = 12$

b The pet store has 9 puppies. Each
much water do all 9 of the puppi

9×6 or $9 + 9$

54

My equation: ___9×6___

Equations:

$3 + 3 + 3 + 3 + 3 + 3 = 18$

$6 + 6 + 6 = 18$

$6 \times 3 = 18$

$(3 \times 3) + (3 \times 3) = 18$

6 The rectangles below have already be
dimensions of each and then find the
found the area of each.

Equations:

$5 + 5 + 5 + 5 + 5 + 5 + 5 + 5 = 40$

$8 + 8 + 8 + 8 = 40$

$8 \times 5 = 40$

ex

9

2

$(10 \times 2) + (10 \times 2) = 40$

a

6

3

Area = ___18___ square units

Equations:

$6 + 6 + 6 = 18$ $3 \times 6 = 18$

en write a related division equation.

b $3 \times$ _8_ = 24	_24_ ÷ _8_ = _3_
d _5_ $\times 9 = 45$	_45_ ÷ _9_ = _5_
f $8 \times$ _4_ = 32	_32_ ÷ _4_ = _8_

(continued on next page)

© The Math Learning Center | mathlearningcenter.org

NAME _____ | DATE _____

Playing with Area page 2 of 2

3 Frank bought a rug for his room. It is 5 feet by 3 feet. What is the total area of the rug in square feet? Use labeled sketches, numbers, or words to solve this problem. Show all your work.

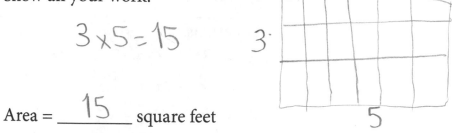

$3 \times 5 = 15$

Area = ___15___ square feet

4 The tumbling mats in the gym are each 10 feet by 8 feet. Miranda pushed 2 of the mats together so she would have enough room to do her routines. Use the sketch below to help find the total area of the 2 mats in square feet. Show your work.

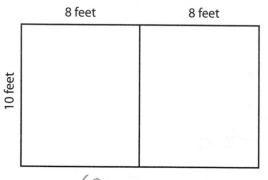

Area = ___600___ square feet

5 **CHALLENGE** Andrea got some free carpet squares at a carpet store. Each carpet square has an area of 1 square foot. She got enough blue squares to cover a space on her bedroom floor that is 2 feet by 8 feet. She got enough red squares to cover another space on her bedroom floor that is 5 feet by 8 feet.

a How many total square feet can be covered if Andrea puts these carpet squares together? Show your work. Use another piece of paper if you need more room.

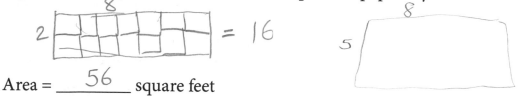

= 16

Area = ___56___ square feet

b There are two equations below you could use to help solve this problem. Mark both of them.

○ $(2 + 8) \times (5 + 8) = a$ ● $(2 \times 8) + (5 \times 8) = a$

○ $(2 + 5) + 8 = a$ ○ $(2 + 5) \times 8 = a$

Triangles & Two-Digit Addition Review page 1 of 2

1 What is the same about all of these triangles?

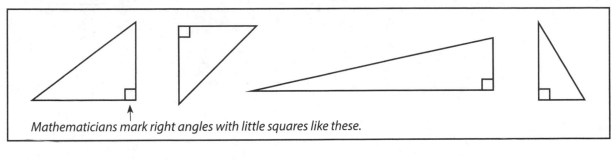

Mathematicians mark right angles with little squares like these.

All the triangles _____

2 a All of the triangles in group A have something in common. Fill in the circle next to the triangle that belongs with them.

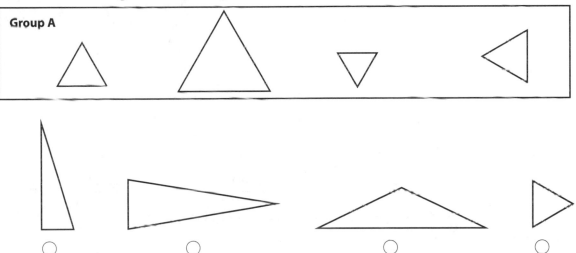

b How do you know the triangle you picked belongs in group A?

3 What do these three triangles have in common?

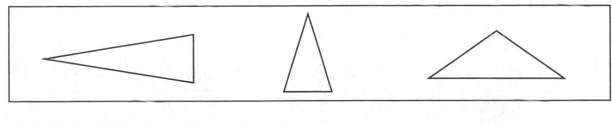

All of the triangles _____

(continued on next page)

  101

NAME _____ | **DATE** _____

Triangles & Two-Digit Addition Review page 2 of 2

4 Add each pair of numbers. Show all your work.

$60 + 35 =$ _____ $27 + 61 =$ _____ $36 + 45 =$ _____

$$\begin{array}{r} 53 \\ + 64 \\ \hline \end{array} \qquad \begin{array}{r} 48 \\ + 93 \\ \hline \end{array} \qquad \begin{array}{r} 42 \\ + 68 \\ \hline \end{array} \qquad \begin{array}{r} 79 \\ + 78 \\ \hline \end{array} \qquad \begin{array}{r} 98 \\ + 19 \\ \hline \end{array}$$

$$\begin{array}{r} 65 \\ + 97 \\ \hline \end{array} \qquad \begin{array}{r} 58 \\ + 72 \\ \hline \end{array} \qquad \begin{array}{r} 21 \\ + 99 \\ \hline \end{array} \qquad \begin{array}{r} 95 \\ + 83 \\ \hline \end{array} \qquad \begin{array}{r} 67 \\ + 92 \\ \hline \end{array}$$

5 **CHALLENGE** Fill in the missing digits.

$$\begin{array}{r} \blacksquare\,8 \\ + 6\,\blacksquare \\ \hline \blacksquare\,0\,3 \end{array} \qquad \begin{array}{r} \blacksquare\,4 \\ + 5\,\blacksquare \\ \hline \blacksquare\,4\,3 \end{array} \qquad \begin{array}{r} \blacksquare\,\blacksquare \\ + 7\,7 \\ \hline 1\,0\,6 \end{array} \qquad \begin{array}{r} 8\,7 \\ + \blacksquare\,\blacksquare \\ \hline 1\,3\,5 \end{array}$$

NAME _____ | DATE _____

🏠 Triangles page 1 of 2

1 Circle the two triangles that are congruent. *Congruent* means exactly the same shape and size.

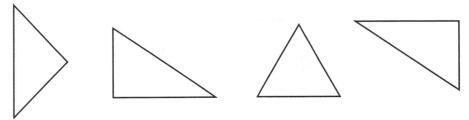

2 Circle the two triangles that are similar. *Similar* means exactly the same shape, but not necessarily the same size.

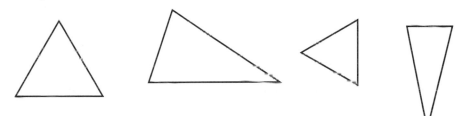

3 Add.

229	448	124	180	229	99	199
+ 71	+ 326	+ 255	+ 352	+ 71	+ 216	+ 699

4 Subtract.

162	148	97	108	203	261	448
− 31	− 23	− 65	− 28	− 87	− 15	− 150

5 Round each number to the nearest 10 and the nearest 100.

Number	Nearest 10	Nearest 100
342		
689		

Number	Nearest 10	Nearest 100
837		
906		

(continued on next page)

NAME _____ | DATE _____

Triangles page 2 of 2

6 Angie and Kara share a bedroom. They've been having trouble agreeing on who is doing her fair share of the cleaning. So they decided to lay a rope on the floor to divide the room in half. Each girl is responsible for keeping half the room clean and organized.

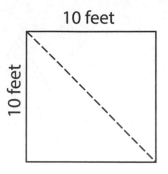

a The area of the whole room is _____ square feet. Show your work.

b The area of each girl's part of the room is _____ square feet. Show your work.

7 **CHALLENGE** Susie and her mother are planting a flower garden. It will be in the shape of a right triangle. They drew a diagram of the triangle and labeled the dimensions. How much area will the flower garden cover? Show your work.

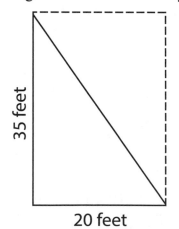

NAME _____ | DATE _____

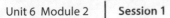 **More Polygons & Time** page 1 of 2

1 Circle the quadrilaterals.

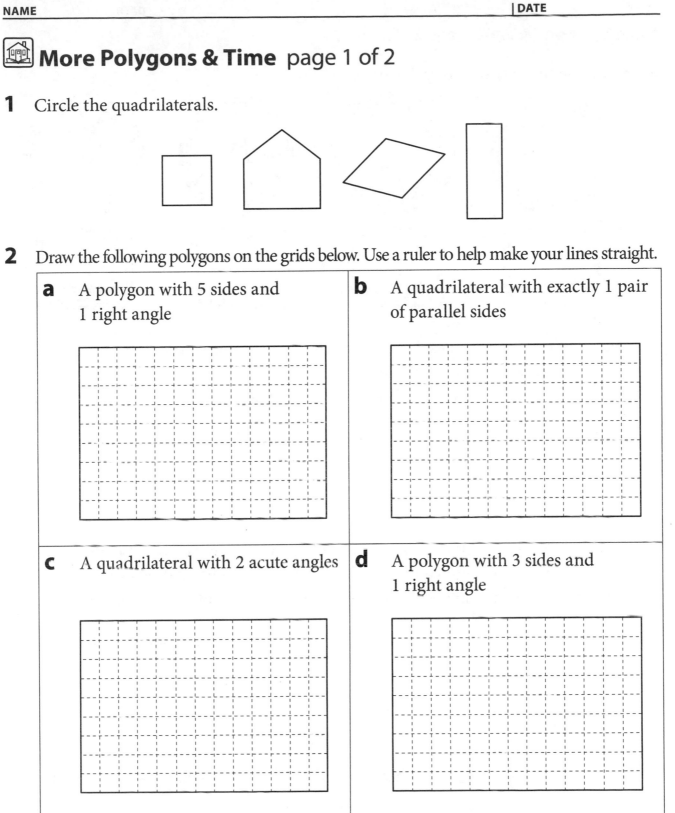

2 Draw the following polygons on the grids below. Use a ruler to help make your lines straight.

a A polygon with 5 sides and 1 right angle

b A quadrilateral with exactly 1 pair of parallel sides

c A quadrilateral with 2 acute angles

d A polygon with 3 sides and 1 right angle

(continued on next page)

NAME _____ | DATE _____

More Polygons & Time page 2 of 2

3 Write the time shown on each clock.

4 Brad likes to bake brownies. It takes him 15 minutes to mix up all the ingredients. Then the brownies need to bake for 25 minutes. After that they have to cool off for 7 minutes. How long does it take Brad to have brownies ready to eat? Show your work.

5 **CHALLENGE** Kevin is building a large model of a soccer ball out of foam board. A soccer ball is made of 20 hexagons and 12 pentagons. It takes Kevin 6 minutes to measure and cut each hexagon, and it takes him 5 minutes to measure and cut each pentagon.

a It will take Kevin _____ minutes to make all the pieces. Show all your work.

b It will take Kevin _____ hours to make all the pieces. Show all your work.

NAME | **DATE**

🏠 Sorting & Identifying Quadrilaterals page 1 of 2

1 A trapezoid is a quadrilateral with exactly 1 pair of parallel sides. Circle the 2 sides that are parallel to each other on each of the trapezoids below. Mark the 2 sides that are not parallel to each other with an x on each of the trapezoids below.

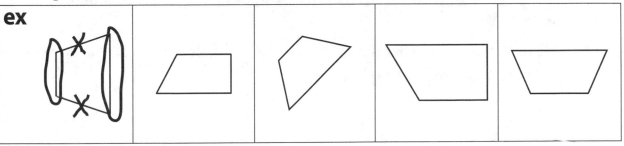

2 A parallelogram is any quadrilateral with 2 pairs of parallel sides. On each of the parallelograms below, circle 1 pair of parallel sides in blue. Circle the other pair of parallel sides in red.

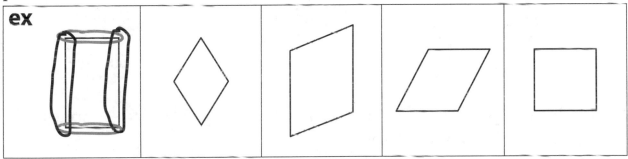

3 Find all the trapezoids below. Color them orange. Find all the parallelograms below. Color them purple. When you finish, you should have 2 quadrilaterals that are not colored.

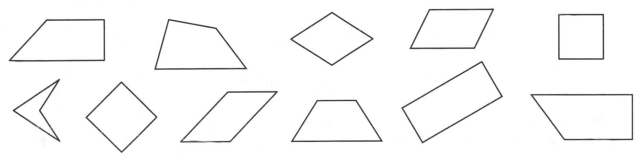

(continued on next page)

  107 © The Math Learning Center | mathlearningcenter.org

NAME | DATE

Sorting & Identifying Quadrilaterals page 2 of 2

4 a This shape is a

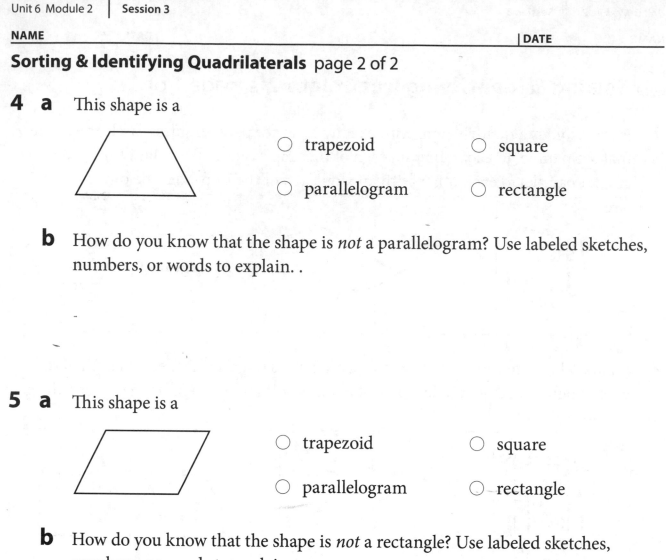

○ trapezoid   ○ square

○ parallelogram   ○ rectangle

b How do you know that the shape is *not* a parallelogram? Use labeled sketches, numbers, or words to explain. .

5 a This shape is a

○ trapezoid   ○ square

○ parallelogram   ○ rectangle

b How do you know that the shape is *not* a rectangle? Use labeled sketches, numbers, or words to explain.

6 a This shape is a

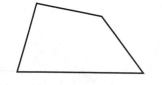

○ trapezoid   ○ square

○ quadrilateral   ○ rectangle

b How do you know that the shape is *not* a trapezoid? Use labeled sketches, numbers, or words to explain.

Quadrilateral Matchup page 1 of 2

1 Draw a line connecting each quadrilateral with its description.

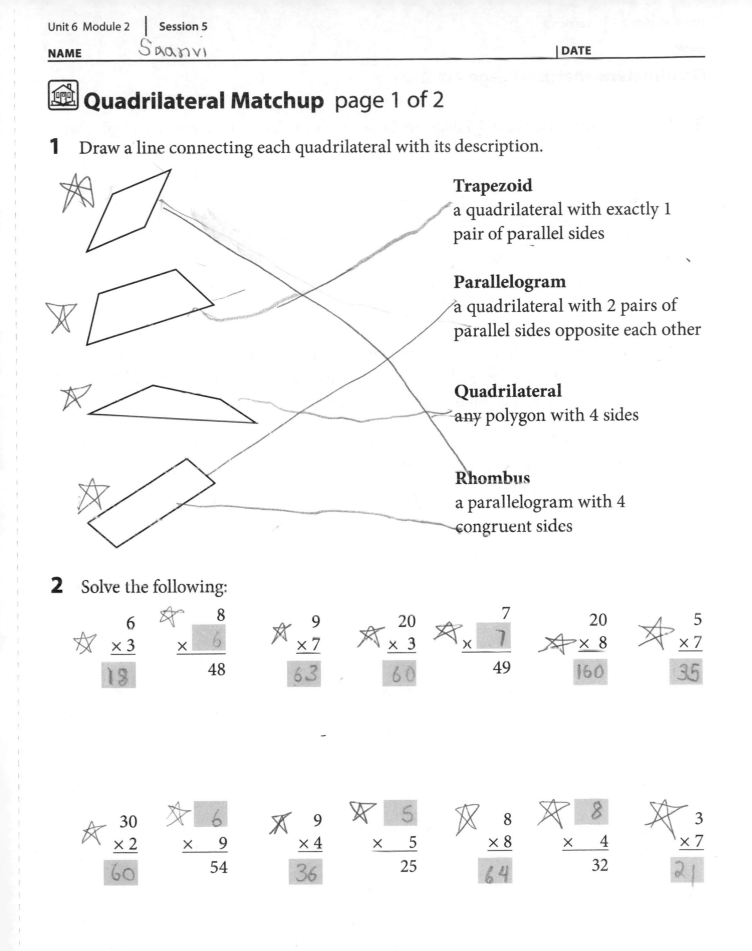

Trapezoid
a quadrilateral with exactly 1 pair of parallel sides

Parallelogram
a quadrilateral with 2 pairs of parallel sides opposite each other

Quadrilateral
any polygon with 4 sides

Rhombus
a parallelogram with 4 congruent sides

2 Solve the following:

$$\begin{array}{r} 6 \\ \times 3 \\ \hline 18 \end{array} \qquad \begin{array}{r} 8 \\ \times 6 \\ \hline 48 \end{array} \qquad \begin{array}{r} 9 \\ \times 7 \\ \hline 63 \end{array} \qquad \begin{array}{r} 20 \\ \times 3 \\ \hline 60 \end{array} \qquad \begin{array}{r} 7 \\ \times 7 \\ \hline 49 \end{array} \qquad \begin{array}{r} 20 \\ \times 8 \\ \hline 160 \end{array} \qquad \begin{array}{r} 5 \\ \times 7 \\ \hline 35 \end{array}$$

$$\begin{array}{r} 30 \\ \times 2 \\ \hline 60 \end{array} \qquad \begin{array}{r} 6 \\ \times 9 \\ \hline 54 \end{array} \qquad \begin{array}{r} 9 \\ \times 4 \\ \hline 36 \end{array} \qquad \begin{array}{r} 5 \\ \times 5 \\ \hline 25 \end{array} \qquad \begin{array}{r} 8 \\ \times 8 \\ \hline 64 \end{array} \qquad \begin{array}{r} 8 \\ \times 4 \\ \hline 32 \end{array} \qquad \begin{array}{r} 3 \\ \times 7 \\ \hline 21 \end{array}$$

(continued on next page)

Quadrilateral Matchup page 2 of 2

3 Oranges cost 25 cents for $\frac{1}{2}$ kilogram. How much would 8 kilograms of oranges cost?

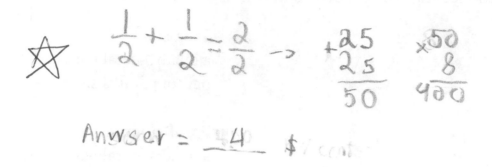

$$\frac{1}{2} + \frac{1}{2} = \frac{2}{2} \rightarrow$$

$$\begin{array}{r} +25 \\ 25 \\ \hline 50 \end{array} \qquad \begin{array}{r} \times 50 \\ 8 \\ \hline 400 \end{array}$$

Anwser = __4__ $ cent

4 **CHALLENGE** Julia wants to bring watermelon for the third grade picnic. Seedless watermelon costs 39 cents for $\frac{1}{2}$ kilogram. One serving of watermelon weighs about 150 grams. There will be 60 people at the picnic.

a How many kilograms of watermelon will Julia need to buy? (Remember, there are 1,000 grams in one kilogram.)

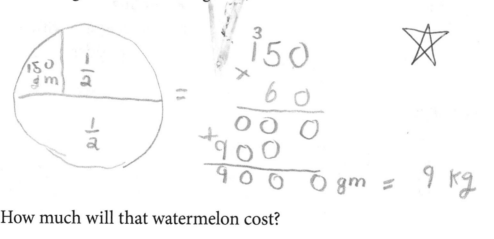

$$\begin{array}{r} \overset{3}{1}50 \\ \times 60 \\ \hline 000 \\ +900 \\ \hline 9000 \end{array} \text{ gm} = 9 \text{ kg}$$

b How much will that watermelon cost?

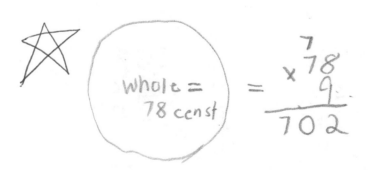

whole = 78 censt

$$\begin{array}{r} \overset{7}{\times 78} \\ 9 \\ \hline 702 \end{array}$$

Ansern: 7.02

NAME _____ | DATE _____

🏠 Perimeter Problems page 1 of 2

1 For the quadrilaterals below, measure in centimeters and label as many sides as you need to find the perimeter. Then write an equation to show the perimeter of the quadrilateral, and fill in the answer at the bottom of the box.

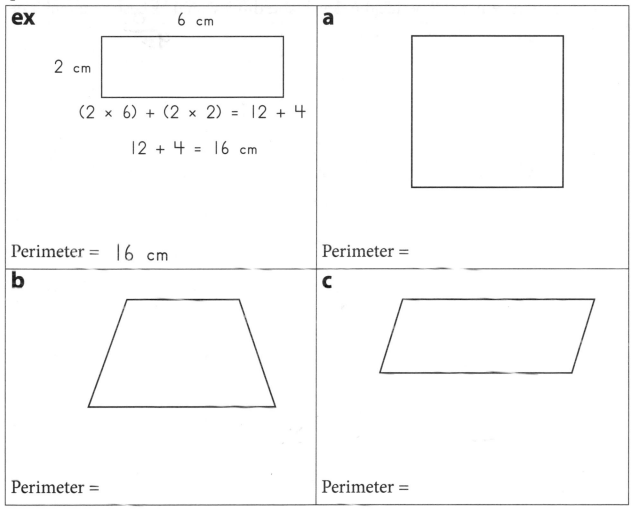

ex

6 cm

2 cm

$(2 \times 6) + (2 \times 2) = 12 + 4$

$12 + 4 = 16$ cm

Perimeter = 16 cm

a

Perimeter =

b

Perimeter =

c

Perimeter =

2 Sarah says you only need to measure one side of a square to figure out its perimeter. Do you agree with Sarah? Why or why not? Use labeled sketches, numbers, or words to explain your answer.

(continued on next page)

NAME | **DATE**

Perimeter Problems page 2 of 2

3 Jacob and his dad are going to make a rabbit pen in the backyard. They have 16 feet of fencing. Help Jacob draw some plans. Sketch and label at least 4 different rectangles with a perimeter of 16 centimeters on the centimeter grid paper below. Write an equation under each sketch to show that the perimeter is actually 16 centimeters. Put a star beside the sketch you think would be best for a rabbit pen.

112

NAME _____ | DATE _____

🏠 Sandbox & Garden Problems page 1 of 2

1 a Mrs. Smith made a sandbox for her kindergarten students. It is 60 inches wide and 125 inches long. Make a labeled sketch of the sandbox below.

b What is the perimeter of the sandbox? Use your sketch to help solve the problem.

The perimeter of the sandbox is _____ inches.

2 Mai and her sister Keiko were planting a garden. They made two beds to plant flowers. One was 4 feet by 3 feet. The other was 5 feet by 5 feet. They want to outline the beds with bricks that are each 1 foot long. How many bricks will they need to outline both beds? Show all of your work.

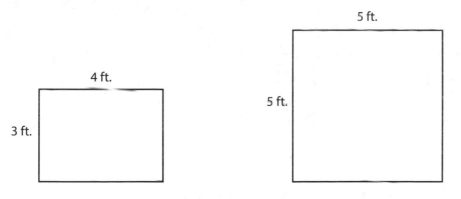

They will need _____ bricks to outline both beds.

(continued on next page)

113

NAME _____ | DATE _____

Sandbox & Garden Problems page 2 of 2

3 DJ Jumpy Frog, who lives in the sisters' garden, says you can also use the number line to show and solve division problems. He says to solve 14 ÷ 2, you start at 14. Then you take equal hops of 2 all the way back to 0. If you count the number of hops, you get the answer.

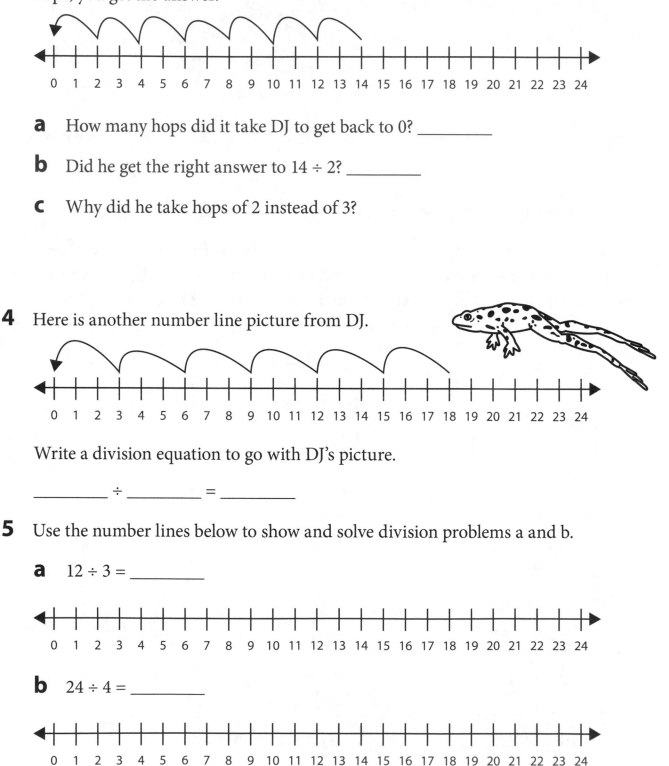

a How many hops did it take DJ to get back to 0? _____

b Did he get the right answer to 14 ÷ 2? _____

c Why did he take hops of 2 instead of 3?

4 Here is another number line picture from DJ.

Write a division equation to go with DJ's picture.

_____ ÷ _____ = _____

5 Use the number lines below to show and solve division problems a and b.

a 12 ÷ 3 = _____

b 24 ÷ 4 = _____

🏠 Area & Perimeter Puzzles page 1 of 2

Show your work for each of the problems below, and label your answers with the correct units.

1 Find the perimeter of this quadrilateral.

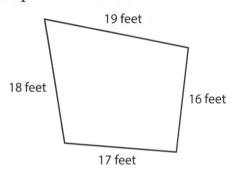

Perimeter = _____

2 The perimeter of this rectangle is 24 inches. Use that information to find the length of the side marked s and the area of the rectangle.

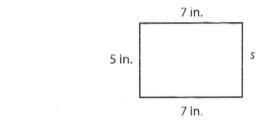

Side s = _____

Area = _____

3 The sandbox at the park is perfectly square. Use the information in the picture below to find the perimeter and the area of the sandbox.

8 feet

Perimeter = _____

Area = _____

(continued on next page)

Area & Perimeter Puzzles page 2 of 2

4 Jake and his mom run laps around the soccer field in their neighborhood. The field is 100 yards by 60 yards, and they run 4 laps around the field each time. When they went to visit Jake's uncle, they did laps around the kids' soccer field in his neighborhood. The field was 30 yards by 55 yards, and they ran 8 laps around it. Did they run more at Jake's uncle's house or in their own neighborhood? Exactly how much more? Show all your work.

5 **CHALLENGE** A rectangle has a perimeter of 36 feet. It is twice as long as it is wide. What are the dimensions of the rectangle? Show all your work.

NAME _____ | **DATE** _____

🏠 Unit 6 Review page 1 of 2

A *quadrilateral* is a shape with 4 sides. Here are some different kinds of quadrilaterals.

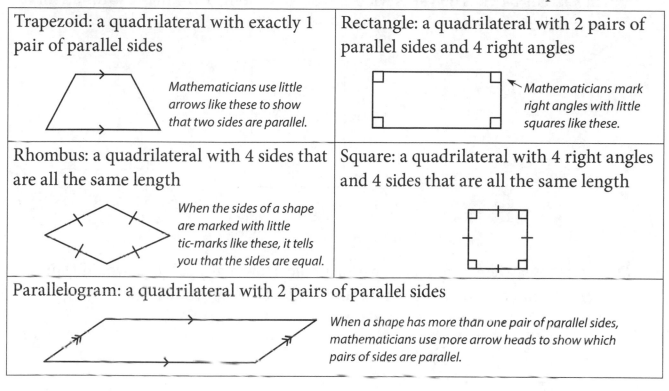

Trapezoid: a quadrilateral with exactly 1 pair of parallel sides — *Mathematicians use little arrows like these to show that two sides are parallel.*	Rectangle: a quadrilateral with 2 pairs of parallel sides and 4 right angles — *Mathematicians mark right angles with little squares like these.*
Rhombus: a quadrilateral with 4 sides that are all the same length — *When the sides of a shape are marked with little tic-marks like these, it tells you that the sides are equal.*	Square: a quadrilateral with 4 right angles and 4 sides that are all the same length

Parallelogram: a quadrilateral with 2 pairs of parallel sides

When a shape has more than one pair of parallel sides, mathematicians use more arrow heads to show which pairs of sides are parallel.

1 Draw in the missing sides to complete each quadrilateral.

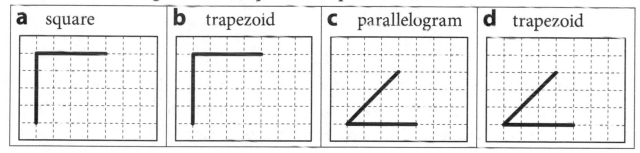

| **a** square | **b** trapezoid | **c** parallelogram | **d** trapezoid |

2 Mayra says that squares and rectangles are parallelograms too, but rhombuses are not. Is she correct? Explain your answer. Use the grid if you want to.

(continued on next page)

Unit 6 Review page 2 of 2

3 a When Danny has lots of extra energy, his mom tells him to do laps around the block. His block is 66 yards wide and 80 yards long. How many yards are in one lap around Danny's block? Show all your work.

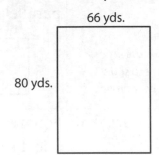

66 yds.

80 yds.

b CHALLENGE There are 1,760 yards in a mile. How many full laps would Danny have to run around the block to run a mile? Show all your work.

4 Danny and his mom are building a fenced region for their dog in the backyard. The region measures 18 ft. by 27 ft. The gate they plan to put in is 3 feet wide. How many feet of fencing will they need? Show all your work.

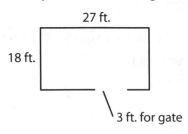

27 ft.

18 ft.

3 ft. for gate

NAME _____ | DATE _____

🏠 Patchwork Fractions & Story Problems page 1 of 2

1 Mark all the fractions that describe the shaded part of each geoboard patchwork quilt block, if the geoboard is 1 square unit.

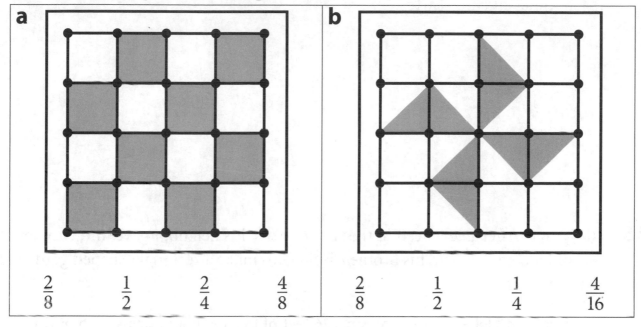

a

$\frac{2}{8}$ $\frac{1}{2}$ $\frac{2}{4}$ $\frac{4}{8}$

b

$\frac{2}{8}$ $\frac{1}{2}$ $\frac{1}{4}$ $\frac{4}{16}$

2 Choose two fractions that you marked in part a above, and explain why they are equivalent.

3 Fill in the bubble next to the equation that will help you solve each word problem. Then solve the problem. Show all your work.

a Kara built a pen for her rabbit. It is 3 feet by 6 feet. What is the area of the pen?

○ $3 + 6 = a$ ○ $3 \times 6 = a$ ○ $6 - 3 = a$ ○ $6 \div 3 = a$

The rabbit's pen has an area of _____ square feet.

b Steve's dog buried 27 bones. That's 3 times as many bones as David's dog buried. How many bones did David's dog bury?

○ $3 + 27 = b$ ○ $3 \times 27 = b$ ○ $27 \div 3 = b$ ○ $27 - 3 = b$

David's dog buried _____ bones.

(continued on next page)

Patchwork Fractions & Story Problems page 2 of 2

4 Lee wanted to put a fence around his vegetable garden. His brother asked him to put a fence around his garden, too. Lee's garden was 5 feet wide and 10 feet long. His brother's garden was 6 feet wide and 7 feet long. How many feet of fencing will Lee need? Show all your work.

5 **CHALLENGE** After Lee fenced in the two gardens, his neighbor gave him another 26 feet of fencing. Lee and his brother decided to make a rectangle-shaped garden for their little sister.

   a Draw and label 4 different ways 26 feet of fencing could be used to outline a rectangle.

   b Circle the rectangle that you think would make the best garden and explain why.

  120

NAME _____ | DATE _____

🏠 Operations & Equations page 1 of 2

1 Solve the addition and subtraction problems.

427	728	246	500	280
+ 92	+ 436	+ 795	– 150	– 145

285	964	835	603	460
– 143	– 528	–297	–465	–235

2 Write a greater than, less than, or equal sign to complete each equation.

36 + 4 **<** 26 + 20   5 × 8 ▢ 10 × 3

12 + 18 ▢ 2 + 28   25 – 10 ▢ 35 – 20

2 × 12 ▢ 2 × 8   1 × 9 ▢ 3 × 4

CHALLENGE

890 – 500 ▢ 756 – 540   400 ▢ 150 + 250

2 × 96 ▢ 4 × 50   1 × 450 ▢ 500 – 50

3 Pick the equation that will help you solve the problem. Then solve the problem. Jake found 32 shells on the beach. He gave half of them to his brother. Then his sister gave Jake 18 more shells. How many shells does Jake have now?

○ (32 × 2) + 18 = ?   ○ (32 × 2) – 18 = ?   ○ (32 ÷ 2) + 18 = ?

Jake has _____ shells.

(continued on next page)

NAME _____ | DATE _____

Operations & Equations page 2 of 2

4 Pick the equation that will help you solve the problem. Then solve the problem and show your work.

a The pet store got 53 fish. They sold 29 of the fish right away. They divided the rest of the fish evenly into 3 tanks. How many fish were in each tank? (The letter f in the equations below stands for fish.)

○ $53 - 29 = f$

○ $(53 - 29) \div 3 = f$

○ $(53 + 29) \div 3 = f$

○ $53 + 29 \times 3 = f$

There were _____ fish in each tank.

b **CHALLENGE** You can get Fantastic Fish Food at the pet store in two different sizes. The smaller size is 60 grams. The larger size is 3 times that much, plus another 11 grams. How many grams is the larger size? (The letter g in the equations below stands for grams.)

○ $(60 + 3) + 11 = g$

○ $(60 \times 3) - 11 = g$

○ $(60 \times 3) + 11 = g$

○ $(60 \div 3) \times 11 = g$

The larger size is _____ grams.

NAME | **DATE**

🏠 **Multiplying by Elevens & Twelves** page 1 of 3

1 Sam and Terra built some multiplication arrays with base ten area pieces. For each of their arrays:

- Label the dimensions.
- Write two different equations to show how many units there are.

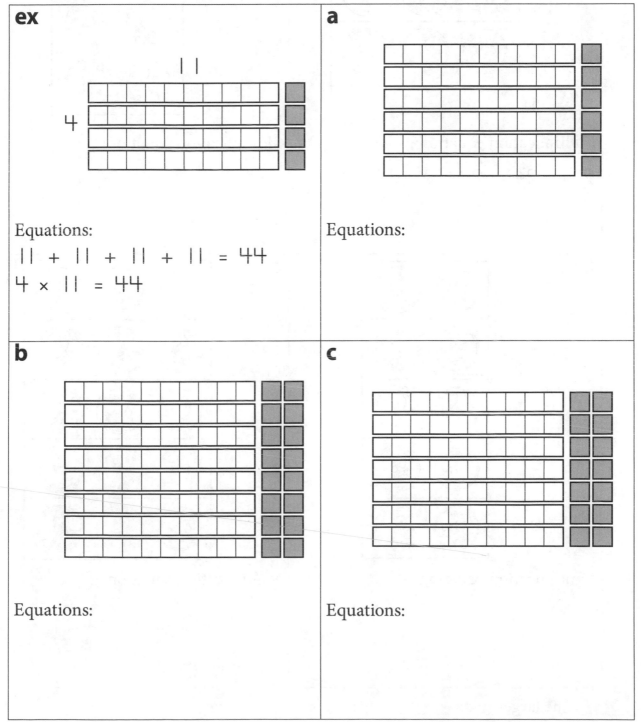

ex

Equations:

$11 + 11 + 11 + 11 = 44$

$4 \times 11 = 44$

a

Equations:

b

Equations:

c

Equations:

(continued on next page)

 123

NAME _____ | DATE _____

Multiplying by Elevens & Twelves page 2 of 3

2 Holly and Micah used dimes and pennies to show some multiplication facts. Write a multiplication equation to show how much money is shown in each arrangement.

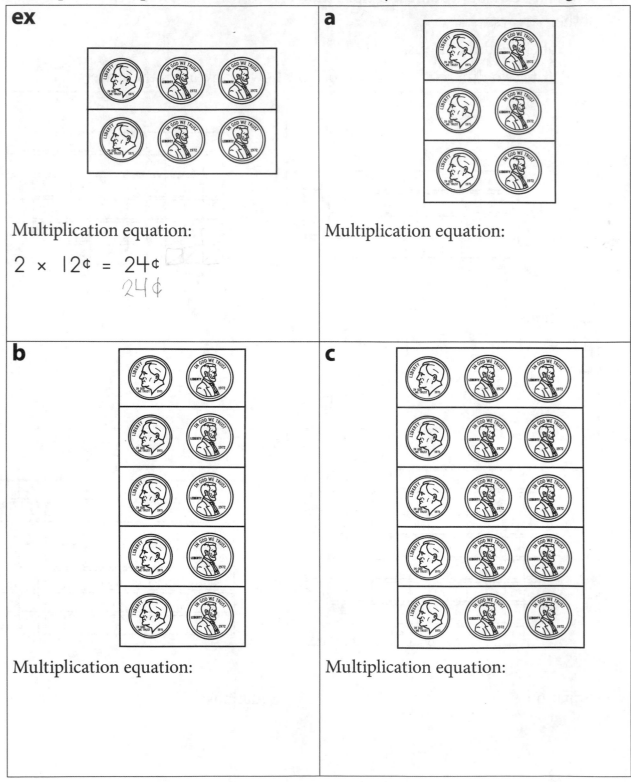

ex

Multiplication equation:

$2 \times 12¢ = 24¢$

24¢

a

Multiplication equation:

b

Multiplication equation:

c

Multiplication equation:

(continued on next page)

  124

NAME _Saanvi_ | DATE _05/9/2022_

Multiplying by Elevens & Twelves page 3 of 3

3 Make sketches of dimes and pennies or base ten area pieces to show and solve each problem. Label your sketches.

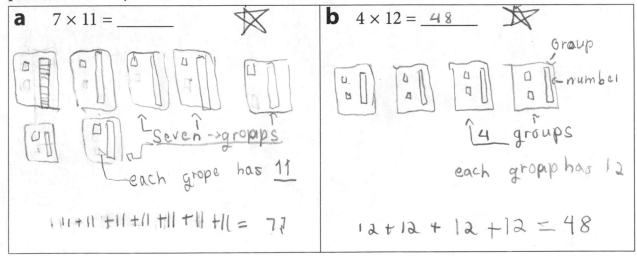

a $7 \times 11 =$ _____

Seven→groups

each grope has **11**

$11 + 11 + 11 + 11 + 11 + 11 + 11 = 77$

b $4 \times 12 =$ _48_

Group ← numbel

4 groups

each grorp has 12

$12 + 12 + 12 + 12 = 48$

4 Use numbers, pictures, or words to solve each of the problems below. Show all of your work.

a King School is holding a bake sale. Jose's mom brought 2 dozen chocolate chip cookies, and Jana's dad brought 3 dozen peanut butter cookies. The helpers took the cookies out of their bags and put them on plates. They put 10 on every plate. How many plates did they need?

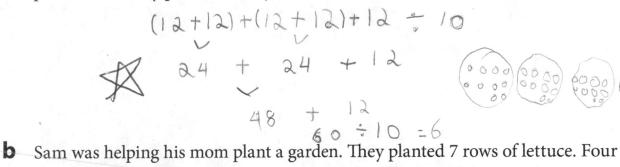

$(12 + 12) + (12 + 12) + 12 \div 10$

$24 + 24 + 12$

$48 + 12$

$60 \div 10 = 6$

b Sam was helping his mom plant a garden. They planted 7 rows of lettuce. Four of the rows had 11 lettuce plants. Three of the rows had 12 lettuce plants. How many lettuce plants did they plant in all?

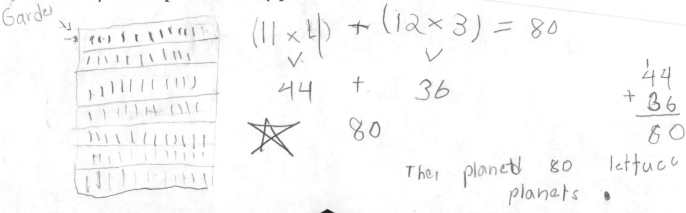

Garde

$(11 \times 4) + (12 \times 3) = 80$

$44 + 36$

80

$\begin{array}{r} 44 \\ + 36 \\ \hline 80 \end{array}$

Ther planed 80 lettuce planets

$$25 \overline{)125}$$
$$10$$
$$2$$

$$3\overline{)125}$$
$$10$$
$$125$$

$$12$$
$$2\overline{)25}$$
$$2$$

```
  3 17
  4 4 0
-  2 9 0
 ─────────
   1 5 0
```

```
    1 1 7
+    2 8
   ─────
   1 4 5
+  1 1 7
  ─────
   2 6 2
+    2 8
  ─────
   2 9 0
```

```
   1 2 4
     9 6
   ─────
   2 2 0
+  1 2 4
  ─────
   3 4 4
+    9 6
  ─────
   4 4 0
```

NAME _____ | DATE _____

Multiplication, Division & Perimeter Practice page 1 of 2

1 Complete the multiplication facts.

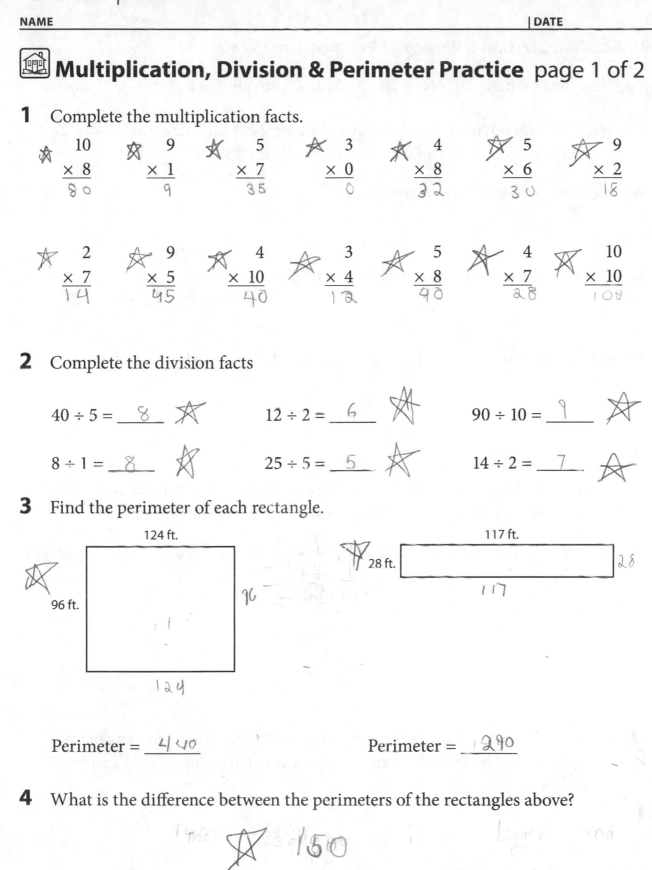

| 10
× 8
80 | 9
× 1
9 | 5
× 7
35 | 3
× 0
0 | 4
× 8
32 | 5
× 6
30 | 9
× 2
18 |

| 2
× 7
14 | 9
× 5
45 | 4
× 10
40 | 3
× 4
12 | 5
× 8
40 | 4
× 7
28 | 10
× 10
100 |

2 Complete the division facts

$40 \div 5 = \underline{8}$ $12 \div 2 = \underline{6}$ $90 \div 10 = \underline{9}$

$8 \div 1 = \underline{8}$ $25 \div 5 = \underline{5}$ $14 \div 2 = \underline{7}$

3 Find the perimeter of each rectangle.

124 ft.
96 ft.
124

117 ft.
28 ft.
28
117

Perimeter = __4⁴40__   Perimeter = __1290__

4 What is the difference between the perimeters of the rectangles above?

150

(continued on next page)

         © The Math Learning Center | mathlearningcenter.org

NAME _____ | DATE _____

Multiplication, Division & Perimeter Practice page 2 of 2

Show all your work when you solve these problems. Use numbers, sketches, or words.

5 Dale and Lori are buying a watch for their father for his birthday. The watch they want to get him usually costs $129 but it is on sale for $60 less.

a How much will the watch cost?

b If they each pay half, how much will Dale pay?

c If they let their brother, Mike, go in on the gift, how much will each pay?

6 CHALLENGE Mrs. Larsen wanted her class to work in groups of 4. After she divided them into groups, there were 6 groups of 4 and 1 group of 3.

a How many students were in the class? Write and solve an equation to represent this problem.

b If the teacher wanted all the groups to be exactly the same size, how many students should be in each group? How many small groups would there be? Show all your work.

🏠 More Multiplication Review page 1 of 2

1 Complete the multiplication facts.

70	60	8	40	7	9	30
× 2	× 3	× 30	× 4	× 10	× 50	× 9
140	180	240	160	70	450	270

50	8	7	40	70	4	80
× 6	× 60	× 50	× 3	× 8	× 90	× 4
300	480	350	120	560	360	320

2 Fill in the missing number in each fact. Then write a related division equation.

$4 \times 5 = 20$ $20 \div 5 = 4$

$7 \times 3 = 21$ $21 \div 3 = 7$

$5 \times 5 = 25$ $25 \div 5 = 5$

$2 \times 7 = 14$ $14 \div 7 = 2$

3 **CHALLENGE** Solve the following:

24	14	14	63	52	10	24
× 2	× 10	× 5	× 2	× 3	× 69	× 4
46	140	75	126	156	690	96

4 Sarah says you only need to measure one side of a square to figure out its perimeter. Do you agree with Sarah? Why or why not? Use labeled sketches, numbers, or words to explain your answer.

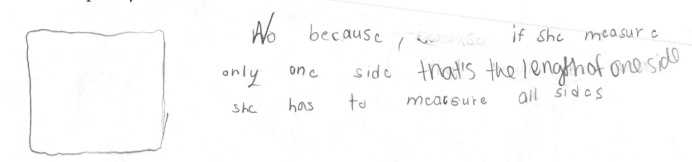

No because, because if she measure only one side that's the length of one side she has to measure all sides

(continued on next page)

NAME _____ | DATE _____

More Multiplication Review page 2 of 2

Use labeled sketches, numbers, or words to explain your answers when you solve these problems.

5 Andrea got some free carpet squares at a carpet store. She got enough blue squares to cover 2 feet by 8 feet and enough red squares to cover 5 feet by 8 feet. How many total square feet can be covered if Andrea puts these carpet squares together?

6 Mark the two equations below that could be used to help solve Problem 5.

○ $(2 + 8) \times (5 + 8) = a$ ○ $(2 \times 8) + (5 \times 8) = a$

○ $(2 + 5) + 8 = a$ ○ $(2 + 5) \times 8 = a$

7 **CHALLENGE** The movie theater in our town has 2 aisles and 3 blocks of seats. Two blocks of seats each have 24 rows of 7 seats. The middle block of seats has 24 rows of 14 seats. How many seats are in the theater in all? Show all your work.

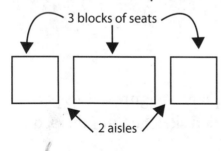

NAME _____ | DATE _____

🏠 Hours to Minutes page 1 of 2

1 There are 60 minutes in an hour. Use that information to help solve the word problems below. For each problem:

- Write an equation to match each problem and solve it.
- Write the answer on the line.

a James stayed at the After-School club for 2 hours on Tuesday. How many minutes was James at the After-School Club?

1 hour = 60   So   we Can repeted 60

✭ two times $60 \times 2 = 120$

$$\begin{array}{r} 60 \\ \times\ 2 \\ \hline 120 \end{array} \qquad \begin{array}{r} 60 \\ + 60 \\ \hline 120 \end{array}$$

James was at the After-School Club on Tuesday for __120__ minutes.

b Kara babysat her little cousin from 4:00 p.m. to 7:00 p.m. on Saturday. How many minutes did she babysit her little cousin?

1 hour = 3 × 60 = 0

✭ 2 8 0

bcauso   4 - 7 equal   3 × 60 = 180

Kara babysat her little cousin for __180__ minutes.

c Carlos started his chores at 9:30 a.m. He finished at 11:30 a.m.. How many minutes did he spend doing his chores?

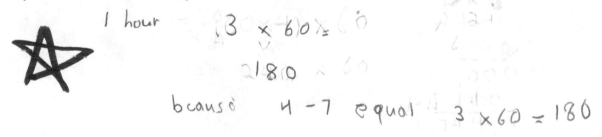

9:30   40

60×2

Carlos spent __120__ minutes doing chores.   **(continued on next page)**

NAME _____ | DATE _____

Hours to Minutes page 2 of 2

2   Mrs. Ramos went out shopping at the time shown on the first clock. She came back at the time shown on the second clock.

8:45   10:13

a   How many hours was Mrs. Ramos out shopping? How did you figure it out?

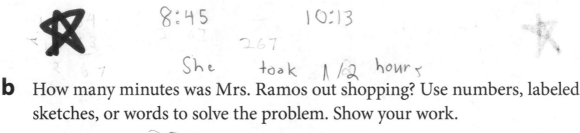

8:45   10:13

267

She took 1 1/2 hours

b   How many minutes was Mrs. Ramos out shopping? Use numbers, labeled sketches, or words to solve the problem. Show your work.

$$\begin{array}{r} 30 \\ 30 \\ \hline 90 \end{array}$$ 90 minturas

3   Fill in the lines with the missing numbers.

3 × 40 = __120__   6 × 60 = __360__   3 × 20 = __60__

5 × 50 = __250__   60 × __50__ = 300   4 × __30__ = 120

20 × __40__ = 80   30 × __7__ = 210   50 × __3__ = 150

4   **CHALLENGE** Are the expressions below equal? If they are, put an = sign in the space. If they aren't, put ≠ in the space. (The symbol ≠ means not equal.)

30 × 60 __≠__ 2 × 90   40 × 3 __≠__ 20 × 4   60 × 4 __=__ 80 × 3

🏠 Telling Time to the Minute page 1 of 2

1 Fill in the circle next to the time shown on each clock.

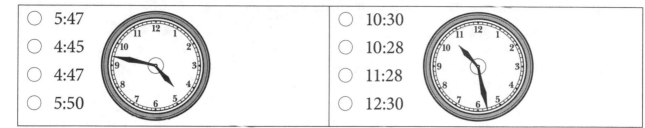

- ○ 5:47
- ○ 4:45
- ○ 4:47
- ○ 5:50

- ○ 10:30
- ○ 10:28
- ○ 11:28
- ○ 12:30

2 Write the time shown on each clock.

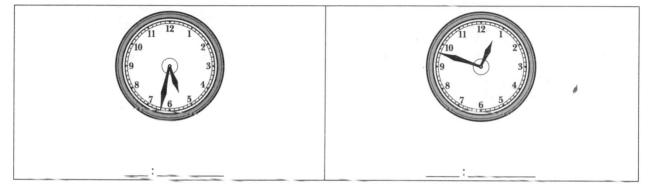

_____ : _____   _____ : _____

3 Circle the digital clock that shows the same time as this analog clock.

4 **CHALLENGE** What fraction of a clock is represented if the hands are at 12 and 3?

(continued on next page)

NAME _____ | DATE _____

Telling Time to the Minute page 2 of 2

Show your work when you solve these problems.

5 Konnel is saving money to buy a chemistry set. He has saved $50 so far. That's $\frac{1}{3}$ of the cost of the chemistry set.

a How much does the chemistry set cost?

b How much more money does Konnel need to save to have $\frac{1}{2}$ the cost of the chemistry set?

6 **CHALLENGE** In marathon swimming, athletes swim distances of 10 km or more. Just like in running, swimmers can swim half-marathons and quarter-marathons as well.

a If a marathon swim is 10 km, how many meters would you swim in a half-marathon?

b How many meters would you swim in a quarter-marathon?

NAME _____ | DATE _____

Division & Fractions page 1 of 2

1 Complete the division facts.

20 ÷ 5 = _____   20 ÷ 10 = _____   18 ÷ 2 = _____

18 ÷ 3 = _____   18 ÷ 6 = _____   18 ÷ 9 = _____

2 Divide each set into equal groups. Shade in some circles as directed.

ex Shade in $\frac{3}{5}$ of the circles. Hint: Divide the set into 5 groups.	Shade in $\frac{2}{10}$ of the circles. Hint: Divide the set into 10 equal groups.
Shade in $\frac{1}{2}$ of the circles. Hint: Divide the set into 2 equal groups.	Shade in $\frac{2}{6}$ of the circles. Hint: Divide the set into 6 equal groups.
Shade in $\frac{1}{3}$ of the circles. Hint: Divide the set into 3 equal groups.	Shade in $\frac{4}{9}$ of the circles. Hint: Divide the set into 9 equal groups.

3 a Find two fractions above that are equal. Write them here.

b How do you know the fractions are equal?

4 Write each of these fractions where they belong on the number line: $\frac{1}{2}$, $1\frac{1}{4}$, $\frac{1}{3}$, $1\frac{3}{4}$

```
◄———————————————|———————————————————————|————————►
    0                       1                       2
```

(continued on next page)

Division & Fractions page 2 of 2

5 Daniel, Emilia, Mía, and Aarón were picking pears in their grandparents' orchard. They had each picked the same number of pears at lunch time, when their grandpa gave them each 6 more pears. Now the four kids had 80 pears in all.

a How many pears did each child have before their grandpa gave them more? Show your work.

b Mark the equation that could help you solve problem 5a.
- $p + 6 + 4 = 80$
- $80 - (6 \times 4) = p$
- $80 = (6 \times 4) + (p \times 4)$
- $(80 \div 4) + 6 = p$

c Write an equation that shows another way to solve the problem. Use h for the unknown number.

6 The next day, the kids went to a nut orchard and picked up 220 hazelnuts. They gave $\frac{1}{4}$ of the hazelnuts to their neighbor and their mother used $\frac{2}{4}$ of the hazelnuts in muffins. The rest of the hazelnuts were saved for snacks.

a How many hazelnuts went into the muffins? Show your work.

b How many hazelnuts did the family have for snacking? Show your work.

🏠 Quadrilaterals & Fractions page 1 of 2

1 Fill in the bubble to show the answer. Then write an explanation.

a This shape is a:

○ trapezoid   ○ square   ○ parallelogram   ○ rectangle

b Explain why:

c How do you know that the shape in the problem above is *not* a rectangle? Use labeled sketches, numbers or words to explain.

2 a Write these fractions where they belong on the number line below:

$$\frac{4}{6} \quad \frac{2}{6} \quad \frac{6}{6} \quad \frac{3}{6} \quad \frac{1}{3} \quad \frac{2}{3}$$

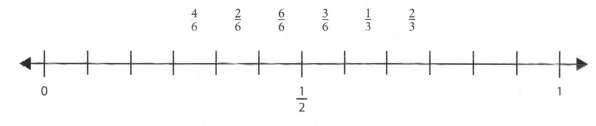

0                          $\frac{1}{2}$ 1

b Name two pairs of equivalent fractions from the number line above.

_____ = _____ and _____ = _____

c What fraction is equivalent to 1 on the number line above? _____ = 1

3 a Write in fractions on the number line below:

0   1

b Name two equivalent fractions from the number line above.

_____ = _____

c **CHALLENGE** Write in a fraction for 1 on the number line for problem 3a.

(continued on next page)

NAME _____ | DATE _____

Quadrilaterals & Fractions page 2 of 2

4 Jenny worked on her homework from 6:15 until 7:15 last night. Spelling took $\frac{1}{6}$ of the time; math took $\frac{1}{3}$ of the time and reading took $\frac{1}{2}$ of the time.

    a Jenny spent _____ minutes on spelling.

    b Jenny spent _____ minutes on math.

    c Jenny spent _____ minutes on reading.

5 **CHALLENGE** The students at Shady Cove School voted for a school mascot. Half the votes went to the Pilots and Mariners, with the Mariners getting 30 more votes than the Pilots. The Eagles got 60 votes and the Dolphins got twice as many votes as the Eagles.

    a What is the new mascot of Shady Cove School? How do you know?

    b How many students voted? Show your work.

NAME | DATE

🏠 More True or False Challenges page 1 of 2

1 An equation is true if both sides are equal. It is false if both sides are not equal. Circle true or false for each equation. You do not need to explain all your answers.

Equation	Circle One		Optional Explanation
ex $18 - 3 = 5 \times 3$	Ⓣ	F	$18 - 3$ is 15 and $5 + 5 + 5 = 15$
a $5 + 8 = 3 \times 4$	T	F	
b $6 \times 4 = 3 \times 8$	T	F	
c $20 - 10 = 20 \div 2$	T	F	
d $8 + 8 = 4 \times 5$	T	F	
e $5 + 7 = 20 - 8$	T	F	

2 Use <, >, or = to complete each equation.

ex $32 + 876$ ⃞ $>$ $870 + 24$ **a** $100 \div 10$ ⃞ $100 \div 5$

b 6×7 ⃞ 5×8 **c** $478 - 138$ ⃞ $678 - 132$

3 Pick the equation that will help you solve the problem. Then solve the problem.

a Josh got 7 toy cars from each of his 4 brothers. He gave 12 cars to his friend. How many cars did he have left?

- ○ $7 + 4 - 12 = c$
- ○ $(7 \times 4) - 12 = c$
- ○ $(7 \times 12) - 4 = c$

b Josh has _____ cars left.

4 Pick the equation that will help you solve the problem. Then solve the problem.

a Sarah left her house at 3:00. It took her 15 minutes to go to the bank. Then it took her 20 minutes to do some shopping. Then it took 15 minutes to drive home. What time did Sarah get home?

- ○ $300 - 15 - 20 - 15 = m$
- ○ $15 + 20 - 15 = m$
- ○ $15 + 20 + 15 = m$

b Sarah got home at _____.

(continued on next page)

NAME _____ | DATE _____

More True or False Challenges page 2 of 2

Use labeled sketches, numbers, or words to show your work on these problems.

5 Sage's Aunt Barbara is making her famous orange spongecake for a party. The recipe requires 5 eggs and makes a cake that will serve 8 people. 72 people will be at the party.

a How many cakes should Aunt Barbara make?

b How many dozens of eggs will she need to make that many cakes?

c How many eggs will be left over?

6 **CHALLENGE** Cameron is having a birthday party. His father bought a baseball cap for every party guest. He didn't buy a cap for Cameron because he already had one. The baseball caps cost $5.95 each. Cameron's dad spent $71.40 on the caps. How many kids came to the party?

NAME | DATE

🏠 Looking for Bridges page 1 of 2

Note to Families

We are beginning a unit of study about bridges. Please take some time to locate examples of the three kinds of bridges shown below. You can find them in your neighborhood, or you could take a drive around your town or city. If you have access to the Internet, you could also find examples online. You might also find examples in books at home or the library. For each bridge, record its name, location, type (beam, arch, or suspension), span length (an estimation will do), and other special features on the table on the back of this sheet.

Three Basic Kinds of Bridges

Beam Bridge

A beam bridge is constructed of a beam supported by at least two abutments or columns. Beam bridges tend to be simple and relatively inexpensive to build. They are most useful for bridging short spans.

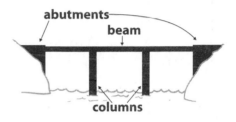

Arch Bridge

An arch bridge is made of an arch between two abutments. It may be made of just one arch between two abutments or of many arches, columns, and abutments linked together, which is called an arcade.

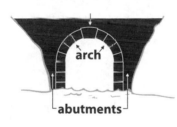

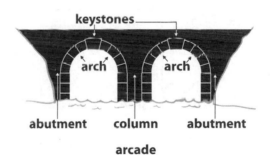

Suspension Bridge

Suspension bridges are made of roadways suspended from cables and suspenders that hang from towers. The cables extend all the way from an anchorage at one end of the bridge to another anchorage at the other end of the bridge. They are the most expensive kind of bridge to build and are capable of spanning the greatest distances.

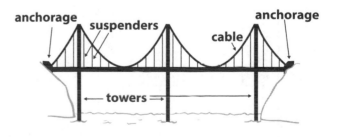

(continued on next page)

NAME _____ | DATE _____

Looking for Bridges page 2 of 2

Name	Location	Type	Span	Special Features

Some additional information that we learned together:

NAME _____ | DATE _____

 Comparing Mass page 1 of 2

1 The table shows the mass of different types of balls used in sports. Use the table to answer the questions below.

Type of Ball	Mass
Ping pong ball	3 g
Baseball	150 g
Basketball	600 g
Soccer ball	420 g
Football	430 g
Volleyball	270 g
Golf ball	45 g
Tennis ball	57 g
Bowling ball	9 kg

a Which ball has the most mass?

b Which two balls are closest in mass?

c What is the difference in mass between the bowling ball and the basketball? Show your work.

d Do two tennis balls have more mass or less mass than a baseball?

e How many ping pong balls equal the mass of one golf ball? Show your work.

Comparing Mass page 2 of 2

2 Solve the problems. Show all your work.

a The Arctic Animals Zoo's female caribou has a mass of 82 kg. The female polar bear's mass is 161 kg. How much more massive is the polar bear than the caribou?

b The zookeeper says that a wolverine's mass is 3 times as much as that of an arctic hare. If a typical arctic hare has a mass of 5 kg, what is the mass of a typical wolverine?

c The refrigerator where the black bear's food is stored holds 35 kg of food. If the bear eats 5 kg of food a day, how many days' worth of bear food can be stored in the refrigerator?

d **CHALLENGE** The Arctic Animals Zoo is planning a new habitat for 4 arctic wolves. Each wolf eats about 2 kilograms of food per day. How much food does the zookeeper need to have ready for the wolves' first 7 days at the zoo?

NAME _____ | DATE _____

Finding Area & Perimeter page 1 of 3

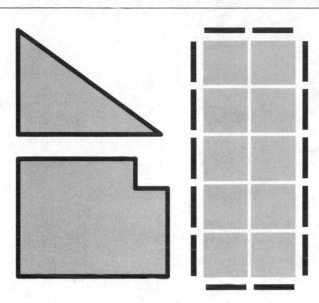 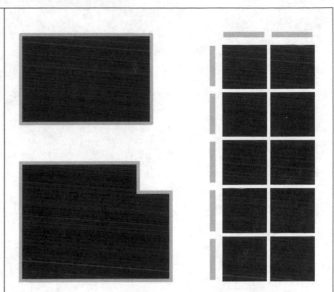

Perimeter is the distance all the way around a figure. Perimeter is measured in linear units like centimeters, meters, inches, and feet.

Area is the amount of surface a figure covers. Area is measured in square units like square centimeters, square meters, square inches, and square feet.

You can use any ruler or measuring tape marked in centimeters for this assignment, or cut out the centimeter ruler below. Keep the ruler for use in future assignments.

1cm 2 3 4 5 6 7 8 9 10 11 12 13 14 15 16 17 18

(continued on next page)

NAME | **DATE**

Finding Area & Perimeter page 2 of 3

1 Measure the dimensions (length and width) of each rectangle. Label the dimensions, then find the rectangle's area and perimeter using equations. Show your work. The first one is done as an example.

ex

9 cm

3 cm

27 sq. cm

Perimeter: $(2 \times 3) + (2 \times 9) = 24$ cm
Area: $3 \times 9 = 27$ sq. cm

a

Perimeter:

Area:

b

Perimeter:

Area:

c

Perimeter:

Area:

d

Perimeter:

Area:

e

Perimeter:

Area:

(continued on next page)

  147

NAME | DATE

Finding Area & Perimeter page 3 of 3

2 Hector says you have to measure the length of every side of this figure to find its perimeter. Do you agree? Why or why not? Use numbers, labeled sketches, or words to explain your answer.

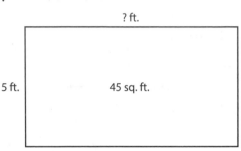

3 This rectangle has an area of 45 square feet. What is the missing dimension? Show your work.

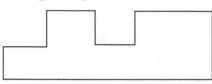

? ft.

5 ft.   45 sq. ft.

4 Alexandra and her dad built a deck in their back yard. The deck's area is 48 square feet and its perimeter is 28 feet. Circle the drawing that shows the deck they built. Use numbers, sketches or words to explain your answer.

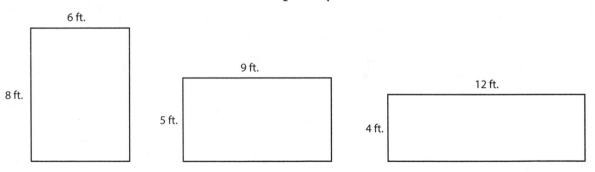

6 ft.
8 ft.

9 ft.
5 ft.

12 ft.
4 ft.

5 **CHALLENGE** For which of these situations would you calculate area? For which of them would you calculate perimeter? Check a box for each one.

Situation	Area	Perimeter	Neither
Finding the number of tiles needed to cover a floor			
Finding out the thickness of the dictionary			
Deciding how many feet of fencing is needed to surround a rectangular yard			
Cutting a strip of tape as long as the whiteboard			
Finding out how much paint it will take to paint one wall of your room			

🏠 Measuring Scavenger Hunt page 1 of 2

1 Look around your home, yard, or anywhere else to find objects that are about as long as the goal lengths in the table below. They don't have to be exact, just as close as you can find. Measure their actual lengths and calculate the difference between the goal and the actual length.

You can use any ruler, yardstick or measuring tape marked in inches, or use the inch ruler to the right. Cut out the ruler if you like. Keep it for use in future assignments.

Goal Length	Object	Actual Length	Difference
$4\frac{1}{2}$ inches			
2 inches			
$1\frac{1}{2}$ feet			
$\frac{3}{4}$ inch			
14 inches			

2 Now look for objects that have an area close to the areas in the table below. Measure the object's dimensions and record them in the table. (You can use the side or face of a three-dimensional object, as shown in the example.)

Goal Area	Object	Dimensions
50 square inches	the side of my toaster	$6\frac{1}{2}$ inches × $8\frac{1}{2}$ inches
4 square inches		
12 square inches		
24 square inches		

(continued on next page)

Measuring Scavenger Hunt page 2 of 2

Footprints

3 An object's *footprint* is the space it takes up when it sits on a flat surface, like the floor or a piece of paper.

a Find an object with a rectangular or nearly rectangular base that you can fit on the centimeter grid below. Place it on the grid and trace its outline. This outline is its footprint.

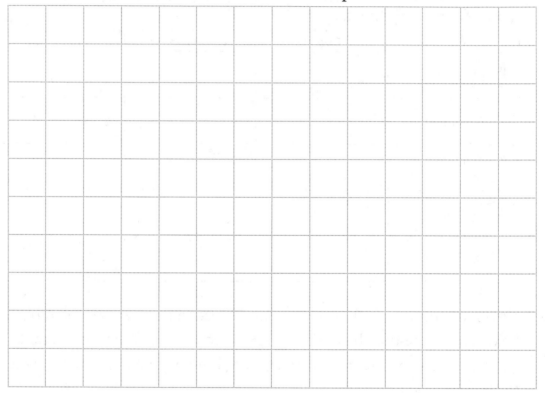

b What object did you choose?

c What is the approximate area of the object's footprint? Show your work.

d **CHALLENGE** If you wanted to store 10 of these objects together on a shelf without stacking any of them on top of each other, how big would the shelf's area need to be?

NAME _____ | DATE _____

🏠 Dividing Shapes into Triangles page 1 of 2

1   Divide the shapes. If you need to, measure to make sure the partitions are equal. You can use any ruler or measuring tape, or a paper ruler from the last two Home Connections.

   a   Draw lines to divide these shapes into two equal triangles. Label each triangle with a fraction to show its part of the whole. The first one has been done for you.

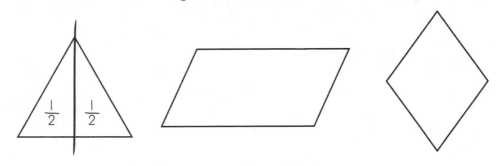

   b   Draw lines to divide these shapes into as many triangles as they have sides. Label each triangle with a fraction to show its part of the whole. The first one has been done for you.

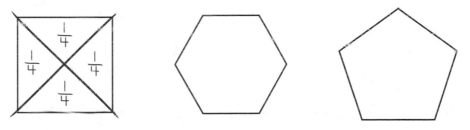

   c   Draw 3 lines to divide the shape into 4 congruent triangles and label each triangle with a fraction to show its part of the whole.

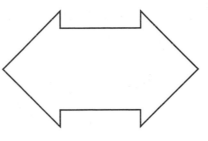

(continued on next page)

      151   © The Math Learning Center | mathlearningcenter.org

NAME _____ | **DATE** _____

Dividing Shapes into Triangles page 2 of 2

2 Draw two shapes of your own, then divide them into equal triangles. Mark each triangle with a fraction to show its part of the whole.

3 a **CHALLENGE** Divide the rectangle into six equal triangles.

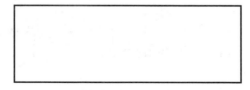

b **CHALLENGE** How many triangles are in $\frac{1}{2}$ of the rectangle?

c **CHALLENGE** How many triangles are in $\frac{2}{3}$ of the rectangle?

152

NAME _____ | DATE _____

🏠 Dress Rehearsal page 1 of 2

Red Barn Theater had a full day of rehearsal, technical work, costume and makeup checks, and other activities the Saturday before the opening night of their big play. Each activity started at a certain time, so people in the theater had to watch the clock to be on stage, backstage, or at other places in the theater at the right times.

1 There is an analog clock in the lobby and a digital clock in each of the dressing rooms. Read the clocks below and write the time to show when each event took place.

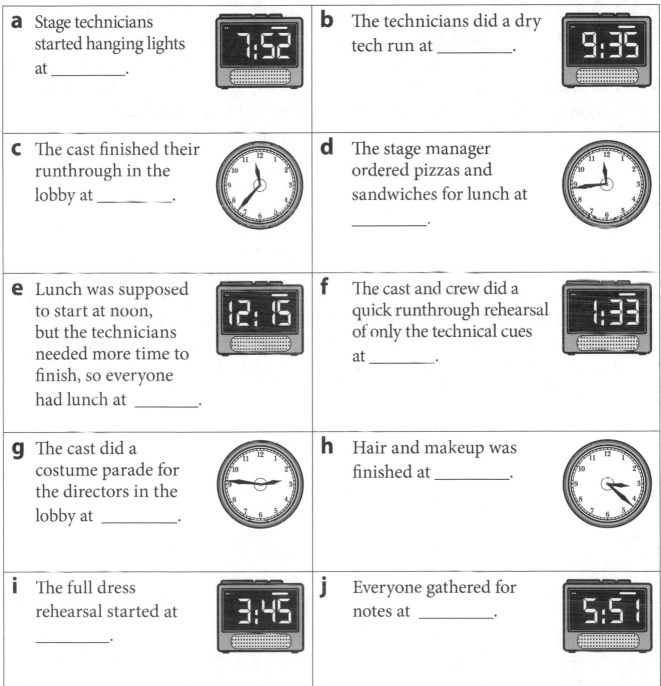

a Stage technicians started hanging lights at _____.

b The technicians did a dry tech run at _____.

c The cast finished their runthrough in the lobby at _____.

d The stage manager ordered pizzas and sandwiches for lunch at _____.

e Lunch was supposed to start at noon, but the technicians needed more time to finish, so everyone had lunch at _____.

f The cast and crew did a quick runthrough rehearsal of only the technical cues at _____.

g The cast did a costume parade for the directors in the lobby at _____.

h Hair and makeup was finished at _____.

i The full dress rehearsal started at _____.

j Everyone gathered for notes at _____.

(continued on next page)

  153

NAME _____ | DATE _____

Dress Rehearsal page 2 of 2

2 Notes begin immediately after the full dress rehearsal is complete. How long did the full dress rehearsal take? Show your work.

3 During dress rehearsal, the show doesn't stop for intermission (they just quickly change the sound and lights for practice). During a public performance, the show will have a 15-minute intermission. How would the stage manager calculate the full time of the show including intermission? Write an equation to show your thinking. You can use letters in your equation to stand for unknown amounts.

4 As soon as notes are done, the cast and crew put everything away and clean up the theater. After cleanup, everyone goes out for dinner. Notes took 18 minutes, and the cast and crew went out to dinner at 7:05. How long did it take for them to clean up? Show your work.

NAME _____ | **DATE** _____

🏠 **Garden Shop** page 1 of 2

1 Casey works at the garden store, and one job he does there is to stock the shelves. Yesterday he had 27 cans of plant food to stock, so he put an equal number of cans on each of 3 empty shelves. Later that day, Tammy came by and bought 2 cans of plant food from the bottom shelf. A little while after that, Shane dropped in and bought 6 cans of plant food—3 from the top shelf and 3 from the middle shelf. Right before closing time, Michael bought 2 cans of plant food—1 from the bottom shelf and 1 from the top shelf. How many cans of plant food were on each shelf at the end of the day?

a Make a drawing or sketch a model to show the situation.

b Solve the problem. Show all your work.

c How do you know that your answers make sense? Come up with a way to check your work and explain it here.

(continued on next page)

  155 © The Math Learning Center | mathlearningcenter.org

NAME _____ | DATE _____

Garden Shop page 2 of 2

2 Owen, Jack, and Kian were shopping for garden supplies with their dad. Their dad said that the kids could split the money he had left after he bought what they needed for the garden. They bought a trowel for $5, two packs of seeds for $1 each, and two bags of flower bulbs that were $4 each. Their dad paid with a $20 bill and a $10 bill, then divided the change among the kids. How much money did Owen, Jack, and Kian each get?

a Write a list of steps you will need to take to solve the problem.

b Solve the problem. Show all your work.

c How do you know that your answer makes sense? Come up with a way to check your work and explain it here.

NAME _____ | **DATE** _____

🏠 Most & Least Fractions page 1 of 2

1 Mr. Wilder bought 36 mechanical pencils to give away as prizes to his students. One-fourth of the pencils were red and $\frac{1}{3}$ of the pencils were purple.

a Were more of the pencils red or purple?

b **CHALLENGE** If the rest of the pencils were yellow, how many yellow pencils did Mr. Wilder buy? Show your work.

2 Ellie made 24 cupcakes to take to her friend's party. She put vanilla frosting on all of the cupcakes. Then she put chocolate sprinkles on $\frac{1}{4}$ of them and red sugar on $\frac{1}{2}$ of them. She left the rest of them plain with only frosting.

a What did most of the cupcakes have on them?

b **CHALLENGE** What fraction of the cupcakes did Ellie leave with only frosting? Use numbers, words, or pictures to show your work.

(continued on next page)

157

NAME _____ | DATE _____

Most & Least Fractions page 2 of 2

3 Shawn is sorting his 12 favorite chapter books by theme onto a shelf. One-fourth of the books are about animals, $\frac{1}{6}$ of the books are about trucks, and $\frac{1}{2}$ of the books are about adventures. The rest of the books are about space.

a Which type of book will Shawn have the least of on his shelf?

b Which type of book will Shawn have the most of on his shelf?

c Does Shawn have more favorite books about animals or about trucks? Write an expression using >, =, or < to show.

d **CHALLENGE** What fraction of Shawn's favorite books are about space? Use numbers, words, or pictures to show your work.

e **CHALLENGE** Does Shawn have more favorite books about animals or about space? Write an expression using >, =, or < to show.

NAME _____ | DATE _____

🏠 Bridge Patterns page 1 of 2

1 Jameson built tiny beam bridges out of toothpicks. He drew sketches of his beam bridges like these:

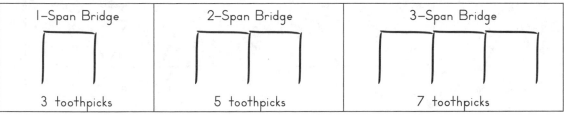

| 1-Span Bridge | 2-Span Bridge | 3-Span Bridge |
| 3 toothpicks | 5 toothpicks | 7 toothpicks |

a How many toothpicks will it take to build a beam bridge with 12 spans?

b Explain your answer using labeled sketches, numbers, and words.

c Fill in the table to show how many toothpicks are needed for each bridge.

Beam Bridge Spans	1	2	3	4	5	6	7	8	9	10	11	12
Number of Toothpicks	3	5	7									

d **CHALLENGE** How many toothpicks will it take to build a beam bridge with 20 spans? Use words, pictures, or numbers to show your work and explain your answer.

(continued on next page)

  159

NAME | **DATE**

Bridge Patterns page 2 of 2

2 Jameson built some tiny truss bridges using toothpicks, too. He made sketches of his bridges like those below.

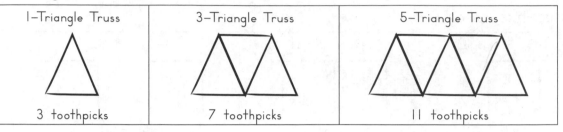

1–Triangle Truss	3–Triangle Truss	5–Triangle Truss
3 toothpicks	7 toothpicks	11 toothpicks

a How many toothpicks will it take to build a truss bridge with 15 triangles?

b Explain your answer using labeled sketches, numbers, and words.

c Fill in the table to show how many toothpicks are needed for each bridge.

Triangles	1	3	5	7	9	11	13	15	17
Number of Toothpicks	3	7	11						

d **CHALLENGE** How many toothpicks will it take to build a truss bridge with 36 triangles? Use words, pictures, or numbers to show your work and explain your answer.

Saanvi Singh

Tanvi Singh